Give Attenda

"Paul has not lost his delight i
death," said John Calvin. He alludec
to reading," written from his pris
that he prepared for death, Paul '

There is his touching message to Timothy as the aging apostle
pleads, "The cloak that I left at Troaz with Carpus, when thou comest,
bring with thee, and the books, but especially the parchments."

Paul leaves no doubt in any mind that Christian preachers and
teachers ought to be readers.

Of course there is always the danger of reading too much and thinking too little. Too much reading, however, is not a fault that many
American pastors have taken time to acquire.

A visiting English preacher observed: "In America every minister
has a fine car and a television set. He seems always to be talking on the
telephone or rushing somewhere. But your ministers do not have
libraries. In England our clergy do not have fine cars and usually no
telephone, but our ministers do have libraries."

"Sell your shirt and buy books," was a motto that helped make
Scotland a land of great preachers.

But the truth is, many a minister simply cannot afford to buy the
necessary books. Therefore, every church ought to put into its budget,
each year, a substantial sum for the purchase of books for its pastor. If
this is not made an item in the budget, as it ought to be, then his congregation ought to give the pastor money earmarked "for the purpose
of books." Books will enrich his mind, illumine his soul, and enliven his
preaching. "Much reading doth make a full man," said Bacon.

In this respect, Catholics are far more alert and logical than Protestants. A Catholic publishing house writes to every Catholic: "Dear
Catholic Readers: Wish a merry Christmas the Catholic way. Give
Catholic books to everyone. Catholic books are among the best books
that offer something of your most precious possession — your faith."

Do not be surprised if your Catholic friends present you with a
Catholic book. They are instructed to do so. Then why should not Protestants purchase and scatter books of the Gospel of redemption and
of freedom among their friends, too.

The Communists make tremendous gains by promoting their books.
It is time to scatter Christian books like the leaves of the autumn.
When we buy a book on the Christian faith and give it to a non-
believer, we are sending out a missionary. The Christian church must
be a "propagandist society."

Lincoln is a classic example of what a few books can do to educate
and inspire a humble personality into greatness. In youth Lincoln read
the Bible through six times. It is difficult to imagine what the history
of America might have been had not that blessed Book been available
to the boy Lincoln.

What better counsel have we after nineteen hundred years than the
dying Paul's admonition, "Give attendance to reading"?

Sure Is Hot!!

Have you ever stopped to think about how hot it is below the surface of the earth? The temperature of the earth rises at an amazing pace as we go toward the earth's center. At about five miles below the surface we find the temperature in the 300° Fahrenheit range. Then we learn that at about 8 miles below the surface, the temperature doubles and runs about 600° Fahrenheit.

At the depth of 11 miles the estimated temperature is over 1000° Fahrenheit. And at 14 miles it is over 6000°!!

I have always believed that Hell could be at the center of the earth. So if this is true, and the temperature gets hotter the deeper we penetrate the earth's surface, then think of the heat at the center of the earth!!

There is NOT but one way to escape Hell -- and that is through Jesus Christ our Lord. He is the only DOOR into the sheepfold. He shed His precious blood upon that cruel Roman cross in order that His blood might cleanse us from sin. Have you been washed in this Precious Blood?

Remember, its going to be unbelievably hot in Hell!!

* * * * * * * * *

"The man who feels no sentiment of veneration for the memory of his forefathers is himself unworthy of kindred regard or remembrance."

-- Daniel Webster

* * * * * * * * *

"The cloke that I left at Troas with Carpus, when thou comest, bring with thee, and the books, but especially the parchments."

-- II Timothy 4:13

* * * * * * * * *

"Only Heaven will determine which was the most important in my earthly ministry -- my preaching or the distributing of books."

-- Peter Cartwright - Circuit Riding Preacher

THE BIBLE MAKES US BAPTISTS

FORMERLY "IN EDITHA'S DAYS"

A TALE OF RELIGIOUS LIBERTY

by
MARY E. BAMFORD

"Reading gives delight, class, and ability; the wise crave it,
the crafty discourage it, and the stupid neglect it."

PHILADELPHIA
AMERICAN BAPTIST PUBLICATION SOCIETY
1420 CHESTNUT STREET

REPRINTED JANUARY 2004
BY
LARRY HARRISON
9066 KNICKERBOCKER
ST. JOHN, IN 46373

FOREWORD

The Bible makes us Baptists, formerly entitled, *In Editha's Days*, is an allegory that becomes an adventure story, laced with real life characters and historically accurate anecdotes. The story unfolds before us through the eyes of a child and grows through her teen years, young motherhood and finally through her progeny. It is a tale of faith, devotion and courage.

The book is also a chronicle of crisis and a manual on martyrdom. It personalizes *FOXE'S BOOK OF MARTYRS*, through the voice and eyes of the narrator, Editha. It is history from a feminine perspective of God's Word coming to the English speaking world. Her travails and trials turn Editha into a genuine heroine.

On another plane, the story professes the truth that the Book of God births Baptists. True Bible-believers and practitioners will eventually become Baptists. I make no apology for this statement, especially after reviewing this book. Baptists do champion the truth of religious liberty that grows from the seeds sown by the Word of God.

I trust after reading this invigorating and enlightening story you will have a greater appreciation for the Baptist faith and the Book that brought us to the forefront. May you never again take for granted the faith we have been endowed with and that was purchased at such great price. I trust God will move you to tears and a strengthening of your commitment to Him.

Evangelist Tim Green
Day Heights, Ohio

LIST OF AUTHORITIES

The author gives the following as authorities for the facts embodied in this story:

ALLEN : "Young Folk's History of the Reformation."
ARMITAGE : "History of the Baptists."
BRAND : "Antiquities."
BROWN : "Memorials of Baptist Martyrs."
CROSBY : "History of the English Baptists."
CREIGHTON : "Age of Elizabeth."
COLLIER : "English Literature."
CHAMBERS ; "Book of Days."
D'AUBIGNÉ : "History of the Reformation."
DE AMICIS ; "Holland and its People."
"Encyclopædia Britannica."
FROUDE : "History of England."
FOX ; "Book of Martyrs."
FISHER : "History of the Christian Church."
GEIKIE : "The English Reformation."
GREEN : "History of the English People."
HAYWOOD : "History of all Religions."
HALLAM : "State of Europe During the Middle Ages."
JOHNSON'S "Cyclopædia."
JONES : "The Baptists."
KEIGHTLY : "History of England."
KNIGHT : "History of England."
LIPPINCOTT'S "Gazeteer of the World."
LITTLE : "Historical Lights."

LLORENTE : "History of the Inquisition."
MOTLEY : "Rise of the Dutch Republic."
MOSHEIM : "Ecclesiastical History."
NEAL : "History of the Puritans."
PERCY : "Tales of Kings and Queens of England."
PRESCOTT : "History of Philip II."
ROBINSON : "History of Baptism."
SWINTON : "Condensed United States History."
SCHILLER : "History of the Revolt of the Netherlands."
YONGE : "History of the Netherlands."

CONTENTS

TO THOSE

WHO HAVE ENTERED INTO

THE HERITAGE OF

RELIGIOUS LIBERTY

In Editha's Days

The One-winged Angel

IN EDITHA'S DAYS

CHAPTER I

THE ANABAPTIST AND HIS BOOK.

"THE angel flew with one wing," whis- 1526
pered Stephen, reverently. A.D.
" Yes," I answered, softly.

We two children stood hand in hand before the
wooden image of the one-winged angel. Stephen
had wished to come to look at him again, but we
were always very quiet when we were there. We
did not wish to disturb anybody in the religious
house ; but it was so strange to see an angel that
had flown into England at one time, bringing a
spear-head, the very same spear-head, the priests
said, that pierced the Saviour's side when he
hung on the cross. All the priests said so. It
would be very wicked in any one to doubt it, and
Stephen and I were sure that it was true.

"Why does the angel stay here all the time?"
I whispered now to my sober cousin. "The
angel might fly again."

Stephen looked at the angel's wooden form, and
thought very seriously for a while.

"Perhaps the angel cannot fly any more," he suggested at last. "Perhaps he has stood so long that he has forgotten how. And it must be very hard to fly with one wing. Cousin Editha, I saw a bird once that had a broken wing, and it could not fly, though its other wing was not hurt at all. How did this angel fly with only one wing?"

But I shook my head in reply. I could not explain. I only believed that it must be so.

"Perhaps," continued Stephen, his forehead drawn into wrinkles with his puzzled thinking, "if I should go outdoors some night I might see an angel fly. Not this angel, because I suppose he likes this place so well that he will never want to fly again, but another angel; and if I do, and if he has only one wing, I will find out how he flies, and then I will remember to tell you, Editha."

There was a little noise, and I pulled Stephen's hand. We went softly out, and hurried away. We were always afraid that some of the priests might not like us to look at the angel, and yet the priests let pilgrims see him. It was like going to visit a person, Stephen and I thought. I do not think that either my mother or Stephen's knew how much we children loved the angel, or how often we went to see him.

Neither my mother nor my aunt would have objected, for they often went themselves, and my mother would sometimes tell us proudly that at the monastery of Hales, in Gloucestershire, she had been shown a vial that a great many pilgrims flocked to see. The priests said that the vial contained some of the blood of the Redeemer, but only those persons who had paid for enough masses could see the blood. All other people would look at the vial in vain, and although my poor mother tried as hard as she could to see the blessed sight, she saw nothing, notwithstanding she paid more money, even all she had. My father had told her that she was foolish to pay money for the sight; but it was always a great source of regret afterward to my mother that she could not see the blood, though she was proud to have seen the vial. My father, from the time I could remember, was always increasingly doubtful of the tales of the monks and the friars, but my mother and Stephen's mother believed everything.

"I might have seen it," my mother always regretfully repeated when she told us children the story of her unsuccessful look at the holy vial of Hales. "I am sure I might have seen it, if I only had money enough to have paid for two or three more masses. I wish I had seen the blood."

But my mother seldom spoke thus when my father was near. She would not talk much before him about such things, knowing that he was doubtful of them. And, indeed, one day he shocked her by saying that he had heard that the "Blessed Bottle of Hales" was only a cheat, made by the priests in order to secure money.

"'The bottle is thick on one side," asserted my father, with indignation in his voice, " so that no one may see into it, and at first the priests keep that side turned toward a pilgrim. But the bottle holds blood truly, I hear, only it is the blood of a duck, and after the priests have told a man to repent and buy masses, and after the man has paid all the money he can, sometimes the priests secretly turn the bottle around, and then of course the man sees the blood. And the poor man is glad, not knowing how meanly he is cheated. But it makes me angry that the priests should be so wicked as to say that it is the blood of the Redeemer in that bottle. The priests— yes, the priests—are liars!"

My father arose in great anger as he ended, and my mother clasped her hands and preserved a shocked silence. She afterward prayed to the saints that my father might be forgiven for making such a statement. But she spoke no more in his presence of the " Blessed Bottle of Hales," though she told us children that the king himself, Henry VIII., believed in that bottle.

"It must be a true relic," added my mother reverently.

I think that my father was very unhappy in those days, for he could not believe the priests, and he hardly knew where else to go for help. Oh, England was so dark then! So many people were stumbling in that darkness. But my mother diligently taught me, so that I believed with great

faith in the one-winged angel of the spear-head,
and in many other false things.

My father, for some months past, had been in
the habit of going to see an old man named John
Eld, who lived in a little hut in our town.   The
walls were of mud and such pieces of timber as
could be laid hold of, and the ridged roof was
thatched over with straw; but then the houses
that Stephen and I lived in were not very large
or good either.

The old man, John Eld, had a book that my
father, who often took me with him, charged me
never to speak about to any one, not even to
Stephen or to my mother.   It was a book called
the "New Testament," and my father said that a
scholar named William Tyndale had written it
out from Greek into English for the English people, and the priests were very angry ; and if they
should ever find out that Neighbor Eld had a
copy of the book, they would come and make
him give it up, and perhaps treat him cruelly, and
so I must never, *never* tell about it.

My father went to Neighbor Eld's to hear him
read the New Testament, and I too listened
eagerly, although I feared it was something
mother would not like to have me do.   But which
was right, my father or my mother? I was
greatly puzzled.

Often when my father and I were there, Neighbor Eld would read to us out of his New Testament a story about a man who went down from

one town to another and fell among thieves, who robbed him and left him half dead, and when a priest came that way he would not help the poor man. And Neighbor Eld would also say that the priest of this story was like the priests now, for they had no pity on poor English souls that sin had left bleeding, and the priests would not come to their help. The priests would even hinder the good Samaritan, William Tyndale, who sought to bring the comfort of the gospel to England. And then my father and old Neighbor Eld would talk of things of which I knew nothing. Once I heard my father say: "I wish I could read as well as you can." And after that Neighbor Eld used to help father about some of the longer words that bothered him in the book. But indeed my father already could read quite well.

But I did not tell my Cousin Stephen anything I heard at Neighbor Eld's. I could keep a secret, if I was only a girl. I knew the very chink in the mud wall where Neighbor Eld hid his New Testament. He covered the hole with a piece of dry mud like the wall, and no one would have known that anything was hidden there. But do you think that I would have told where that hole was?

When Stephen and I hurried away from the wooden angel that afternoon, we ran down the street till we came near its end. A priest was walking there, one we had never seen before. Stephen and I would have run away again, but the priest stopped us and asked us if we knew in which hut a man named John Eld lived. We pointed in the direction, and watched him as he walked toward the hut, not far away.

"Neighbor Eld will not be home," said Stephen softly to me.   "He weaves all day."

But the priest pushed open the door of Neighbor Eld's low hut, and went inside.

"He will not find him," declared Stephen again.

But I was startled by a sudden thought.

"Oh!" I cried ; "oh, if he finds——"

I had almost said "the New Testament!" I stopped, frightened enough to think I had nearly revealed the secret, even to Stephen.

I snatched my hand away from my cousin, and ran toward Neighbor Eld's hut. There was a small hole in one rickety side, a hole through which a person could look from outdoors. I was determined to see what that priest was doing.

"Editha, Editha," called Stephen from the distance, but I did not answer.

I went softly around the little hut and my bare feet made no noise as I stole toward the hole. Cautiously I dropped on my knees, and put my eyes to the crevice in the wall.

I could see somewhat inside, for the priest had left the door a little open to give light. He was evidently trying to find something. He walked around the room, stopping to stir with his stick the straw of Neighbor Eld's bed. He looked very fierce, a id I trembled as he came nearer my place of observation.

"He will see me," I thought in trepidation, and I drew back quickly.

I heard the stick rattle in the corner next me, and I caught my breath   But the footsteps inside the hut passed on, and I put my face again to the hole.

Near the corner toward which the priest was going was the place in the wall where Neighbor Eld always hid his New Testament. Oh, was that priest going to find it? I held my breath in fear, as he struck with his stick here and there, muttering impatiently to himself.

The priest drew nearer—nearer to the spot! There! He was just in front of the hiding-place!

I strained my eyes to see. The priest hastily brushed by the spot, and his mutterings grew louder. I wondered if he was really sure that Neighbor Eld had a New Testament. But the priest did not find it.

"Editha, Editha," called Stephen's voice again. The boy was coming toward the hut, and I did not dare to stay. I sprang softly to my feet and ran swiftly away from the place. Neither Stephen nor I paused untll we came safely to our own homes.

"I will tell Neighbor Eld that a priest went into his house," I resolved, indignant that anybody should trespass upon the old man's belongings during his absence.

But day after day went by, and still Neighbor Eld's door remained shut. He seemed to have disappeared from the day of the stranger-priest's visit. When I told my father of the strange thing I had seen, he looked very grave.

"Did the priests do anything to Neighbor Eld, father?" I asked, struck with fear. "He did read us good things."

My father did not answer, but that day he went to Neighbor Eld's hut, and examined the crevice in the wall where the New Testament had usually been hidden. It was gone! Neighbor Eld and his book had disappeared together. I heard my father murmur to himself something that I did not then understand: "It is hard, it is hard for the old Anabaptist."

What was an "Anabaptist"? and what did my father mean? I had never before heard that word with which I was to become so familiar before many years had gone by. I did not know what Anabaptists had already suffered in England. Nor did I know that it was one charge against the hated and persecuted Lollards that they would not baptize their infant children.

Neither was I aware that he who, nearly one hundred and fifty years before, had translated into English the whole Bible,—which now alas had become almost unreadable, because of the changes wrought in our language,—had suffered the execrations of priest and prelate because of his belief. Some have said that he was an Anabaptist.

CHAPTER II

STEPHEN'S RIDDLE

"I KNOW something," announced Stephen, proudly.

"What is it?" I asked.

We two children were watching a hen that my mother had sent us to feed.

"A boy told it to me," returned Stephen, looking much puffed up by his wisdom.

"What is it?" I asked again.

"It is a riddle," declared Stephen, losing none of his important air. "It is—'What folks are they who live in a cellar all the time, and never eat anything but salt fish till they die?'"

"It isn't anybody," I answered emphatically.

"Yes, it is," contradicted Stephen.

"Who is it?" I unbelievingly questioned.

But Stephen did not know. The boy who had been his informant had told him the riddle, but not the answer to it.

"It is not anybody," I reiterated, with great decision. "Nobody could live in a cellar all the time, and eat nothing but salt fish! You could not yourself, Stephen."

Stephen still remained unconvinced.

That night, when my father came home

from work, and was taking his supper, Stephen's shrill voice suddenly arose, questioning him: "What folks are they who live in a cellar all the time, and never eat anything but salt fish till they die?"

I turned indignantly, with my lips ready parted to reprimand Stephen. I had supposed I had banished such nonsense from his mind. He had not said anything about the riddle since he and I talked it over. I was wiser I thought than he, and no matter if I was only a girl, I felt that he might have believed me when I told him so positively that nobody *could* live in a cellar all the time, and eat nothing but salt fish.

To my great surprise, however, my father suddenly left his porridge, and with a groan that was half a sob, hurried out of the house.

I had caught one glimpse of his face, and he seemed as if about to break forth in tears.

Stephen and I stared blankly at one another.

"Be still!" I fiercely warned my injudicious cousin.

"Why didn't he answer me? What made him go away and cry?" questioned the astonished Stephen, not regarding my admonition.

But I was highly indignant at him for having said anything that made my father feel badly. He did not come back into the house. At last, quite worried about him, I slipped outside into the dark. Father was nowhere near that I could see. I ventured to walk around the house. On

the far side I saw a dark object, and drawing
softly near, I discovered that it was my father.
He was down on his knees, his face hidden in his
hands, sobbing. I caught some of his scarcely
audible words :

"Lord, Lord," he prayed, in broken tones ;
"give me strength. O Lord, my wife, my little
girl! If I follow thee, must they come to death
too? O Lord, thou seest what the priests do.
Oh, help me, help me!"

His form shook, and he looked entreatingly up
at the sky with his hands clasped.

"Father," I called softly; "father."

He turned, and I ran to him. I felt his tears
on my face as I kissed him, but I did not dare to
ask any questions. I did not then know that his
was a soul in the throes of the agony that pre-
ceded decision. Should he blind his eyes to the
truth, and live subject to the priests? Or should
he count not his life dear to himself ; and foresee-
ing from the hatred with which the priests regarded the New Testament what would be the
probable fate of those who firmly held to that
book, yet dare to bravely say, "Lord, I will follow
thee"?

My father and I stood a few minutes in the
night, and then we went into the house together.
I realized that there was something that I did not
understand. Why should Stephen's riddle send
father outdoors in this way?

I pondered for many days on this subject, but I

could not arrive at any conclusion, and I felt it to be an insoluble mystery about which I dared not speak to any one.

And yet had I known it, as I did afterward, there was a cellar in Oxford where something dreadful was happening that very year. Awhile before this, Cardinal Wolsey had transferred a number of students from Cambridge to Oxford, and unknown to him, perhaps, there were four of these new-comers who were zealous Gospellers. And in secret one of them named Clark was in the habit of reading St. Paul's epistles aloud to the other young men when they came to his room. More and more young men came, in spite of Clark's telling them that it was dangerous to do so. One of the young men, named Anthony Delabere, said : " I fell down on my knees, and with tears and sighs besought him that for the tender mercy of God he should not refuse me, saying that I trusted verily that he who had begun this in me would not forsake me, but would give me grace to continue therein to the end. When he heard me say so, he came to me, took me in his arms, and kissed me saying, ' The Lord God Almighty grant you so to do, and from henceforth ever take me for your father, and I will take you for my son in Christ.' "

For about six months the young men had been in the habit of meeting, when a London curate, named Thomas Garret, came back to Oxford to circulate Testaments. But he had been tracked, and orders were given to have him arrested. All that was going on about the New Testament among the young men was discovered. In Clark's room books were found hidden behind the wainscoting, and thus the proof was positive.

Clark and a number of students were put into a cellar in which the butler of Cardinal's College kept his salt fish. The odor of this cellar was dreadful, and the dampness and foul air began to affect the health of the poor prisoners. One day, after the captives had been taken out of the cellar and tried before the judges, a great fire was kindled at the head of the market place, and the prisoners were brought forth, each bearing a fagot. When they came to the fire, they were forced to throw into it the books that had been found in their rooms. After this, the young men were taken back and put into the fish cellar once more. Two only had been released on trial.

The poor prisoners suffered terribly. They were fed on nothing but salt fish, and this of course created a burning thirst. Who could live in such air, amid such odors, fed on such food? As the weeks went by, the young men, wasted to shadows of their former selves, wandered up and down the dreadful cellar. Four of them, Clark, Sumner, Bayley, and Goodman, were weakened by fever, and crawled along, leaning against the cellar walls.

Clark, the oldest of the prisoners, became so weak that he could not walk, unless uphell by

some one else. By-and-by Clark became unable
to walk at all, but lay stretched upon the damp
floor. Feeling that he was about to die, he asked
that he might be allowed to take the communion.
The jailers carried the request to their master,
who refused to allow the dying man such a privi-
lege.

When Clark heard this cruel refusal, he lifted
up his eyes and murmured, " *Crede et mandu-
casti*," " Believe, and thou hast eaten."

Three others of the prisoners were dying also.
For six months, from February to August, the
prisoners had been kept in that dreadful cellar.
No wonder that four were dying! The cardinal
was besought to have pity. At last, about the
middle of August, as the other young men in that
cellar were praying over their four dying companions, the commissioner arrived and informed
them : " His lordship, of his great goodness, per-
mits the sick persons to be removed to their own
chambers."

So litters were brought, and the dying men
were carried out to their rooms. But Wolsey's
clemency did not extend to others besides the four.
The rest of the prisoners yet remained shut in the
fish cellar.

Release came too late, however, for the four
who had been carried out. Several of the mem-
bers of the university tried to save the lives of the
dying young men, but their efforts were unsuccessful.

Their deaths caused Cardinal Wolsey to relent a little however toward the other young men in the fish cellar. Perhaps Wolsey was afraid that people would be enraged against him for permitting the deaths of the four. Perhaps he did have some heart left in him, after all. At least he wrote to his agents at Oxford, concerning the other young men in the fish cellar : " Set the rest at liberty, but upon condition that they do not go above ten miles from Oxford."

And so, wasted and weak, the young men who had endured so much for conscience' sake, came out of the terrible cellar. Their weeping friends ran up to them and helped them to walk away from their place of imprisonment.

My father told me afterward, when I was somewhat older, that many a time during those months he could hardly bear to eat his own meals, so much did he feel pity for those poor young men, shut in that cellar suffering and dying ; and so certain did he feel that if he should persist in reading and following the word, he would bring not only himself but his wife and child into danger.

" How could I sit down to my own meal, and not think of those poor young men, starving in the Oxford cellar ? " questioned my father, when he told me. " But I could not speak to you about it, Editha, that night when Stephen asked me his riddle. How could I let you know what cruel thing was being done ? It was not a tale to tell a

child. It was enough that you should have seen
that priest hunting for old Neighbor Eld and his
Testament."

One of the young men who was in that fish
cellar was John Frith, a great friend of William
Tyndale. Awhile after this, John Frith was
afraid of another arrest, and so he fled beyond the
seas to Tyndale.

My unlucky cousin Stephen soon forgot his riddle of the cellar, and no doubt my father thought
that I too forgot it. But who can tell what
a child forgets, and what she remembers? I pondered the more for my quietness, and I never forgot the look I had seen on my father's face the
night Stephen asked his question. That look fastened the question in my mind.

But I did not know that what my father con-
templated was more than a mere separation from
the church of Rome. I did not know what Anabaptist teaching he had had from Neighbor Eld.
Nay, I did not know what teaching my father
had had from our Lord. None teacheth like
him.

And I think that my father, even at this time,
had begun to realize that he who for conscience'
sake became a Baptist, or an Anabaptist as the
term was, thereby became a person hated above
all others by the Popish priests. He whom the
priests hated let him beware! Rome had cellars
worse than that fish cellar at Oxford! Rome had
the stake and the torture for just such men as the

Anabaptists, those heretics who persisted in refusing to allow their infant children to be baptized
by the priests. This, this was the mark of a
heretic indeed!

But Rome very well knew that no man was apt
to revolt against her rule more quickly than he
who had a Bible and read it. Away with the
New Testament from England! That book made
Anabaptists.

And the Anabaptists talked of freedom of conscience, religious liberty, man's right to read the
word of God, and worship God without compulsion as to manner. Now "freedom," "religious
liberty," had always been the one thing abhorred
of Rome. She strove to make all men her obedient
servants. She wanted no self-assertion, no indi-
viduality, no thinking. Rome could think for
all men. What they should do was *obey*. Why
should any translator of the Bible, any reader of
the Bible, disturb with his ideas of religious
liberty, the order, the convenience of Rome's
system?

"Freedom of conscience," "religious liberty."
No land on earth should have *that* if Rome could
prevent!

CHAPTER III

THE BOOKS DESTROYED

SOMETHING had occurred that same year, a little while before this. Away from our town of Caversham, down the river Kennet, down the river Thames, lay London town. And there at old St. Paul's, before the " Rood of Northen," as men called the crucifix by the great north door of the cathedral, a large fire was crackling and leaping one Sunday in February, 1526.

On a platform above the altar-steps, sat the great cardinal, Thomas Wolsey. Oh, he was a magnificent sight! He wore a purple robe and scarlet gloves ; his shoes were golden, and a canopy of cloth of gold was over his head. Abbots and bishops and friars who were gorgeously dressed in satin and damask were around him ; and within the altar-rails, on the platform, were baskets that were piled with Lutheran books which had been seized by Wolsey's orders.

The sermon was preached by John Fisher, the old bishop of Rochester, who could not be heard because of the disturbance of the great number of people—for the building was full, so full that no more could get in. After the sermon, five men were brought in to kneel down and ask forgiveness

of God and the church and the cardinal ; and then
these men were led three times around the fire before the Rood of Northen, as a warning of what
they might expect to suffer if they said or did anything more against the Romish friars. One of the
five men was an Augustine friar himself, and he
had been threatened with being burned to death
if he did not retract a sermon he had preached.
But as at last he had agreed to come publicly and
kneel down and ask forgiveness, he was not to be
burned. The books that had been taken by Wolsey's men were burned instead, and the cardinal,
with the thirty-six abbots, priors, and bishops in
splendid array, saw the books burned, and then
all these mitred men departed.

They had conquered !

But had they ? Oh, Cardinal Wolsey, you did
not know everything ! You need not have thought
that by burning some books everything would
be made quiet in England ! If you did think that
at all, you were mightily mistaken. For there
was coming to poor, down-trodden, priest-ruled
England, a book greater than any that Luther or
his followers ever wrote. The New Testament
was coming, coming in the English tongue. Oh,
how Cardinal Wolsey hated that such a thing
should come to pass.

It was only a few months after this burning that
the first of Tyndale's English New Testaments
entered England. There were three thousand
printed New Testaments secretly brought into

England, and the bishops had had letters of warning from the continent about them ; but the bishops could not find out who it was that was spreading the books.

The bishops did their best though to keep the New Testaments away. Through the English ambassador, attempts were made to punish the printer of the Testaments, but nothing could be done beyond seizing three hundred copies of the book. The rest of the New Testaments found their way to London in spite of the bishops. No wonder that those English folk who had the New Testaments must be so very careful not to let a single priest know it.

" Father," I whispered one evening after Neighbor Eld's disappearance, " do you think that anybody found out that Neighbor Eld had a New Testament ? "

I had put my mouth close to my father's ear, for I was afraid to ask such a question aloud. It was yet a secret from my mother that I had ever seen such a book.

My father shook his head as if he could not answer my question.

" I miss his reading," he returned, sadly ; " I miss it greatly. I wish I knew how you and I could get a New Testament, Editha."

" So do I, father," I rejoined.

It was partly childish sympathy that made me speak so. Still I often thought of things that I had heard in Neighbor Eld's hut, and I often remembered the story the old man had read about the traveler from Jerusalem to Jericho, and fell among thieves.

I especially remembered that story, because I had heard Neighbor Eld comment on it, and because in my childish mind I contrasted the gospel story with one that my mother had frequently told Stephen and me, about a robber and the Virgin. The robber got his living by going out on the highways and plundering travelers.

"It was wicked in him to be a thief, of course," explained my mother when she told us the story ; "but whenever he went out robbing, he was always careful to pray to the Virgin first. At last this robber was taken, and was about to be hanged, but while the rope was around his neck, he prayed as usual, and his prayer was answered, for the Virgin herself held him up with her white hands so that he did not die, but lived for two days hanging there ; and the man who hanged the robber was astonished and tried to kill him with a sword. But every stroke of the sword was turned away by an unseen hand, and at last the executioner had to let the robber go free, for there was no killing him, because the Virgin heard his prayer. And after he was free, the robber went to an abbey and became a monk."

"Was it one of the monks that live here?" asked Stephen, who had listened very attentively to the story.

"No, no," answered my mother, hastily. "No,

it was no one here. Never think it, Stephen.
None of them were ever robbers."

And so this foolish, monkish tale stayed in my
mind, and I never saw a new priest without re-
calling it. I thought too, of the gospel tale, and
of how I had heard Neighbor Eld say that the
priests would hinder that good Samaritan, William
Tyndale, from bringing the comfort of the gospel
to poor English souls that sin had left bleeding
by the highway.

But my mother would have been frightened
had she known that I had ever seen or listened to
the words of the New Testament, for I had heard
her say that it was only a few years before, during
the reign of the same king, Henry VIII., that
readers of the Bible were compelled to wear the
fagot-badge on their clothes.

I did not then know that William Tyndale, he
who would translate the New Testament into
English, had been obliged several years prior to
go to Germany in order to make the translation;
and that he said of himself : "I understood at the
last, not only that there was not room in my lord
of London's palace to translate the New Testament, but also that there was no place to do it in
all England."

And now that the New Testament had been
translated and printed, what would the bishops
do if they could find the books? Ah, those flames
by the Rood of Northen shone yet in the eyes of
thinking men.

It was those flames that burned the words of the
New Testament into my father's heart.   Yet,
though he believed the truth himself, he could
not help my absorbing many foolish notions concerning the saints.   I remember that one evening
when I was whispering to my father about the
New Testament, I suddenly heard Stephen crying
in the next room.

I slipped from my father's knee, and ran to see
what was the matter with my beloved cousin.

"My tooth aches," sobbed Stephen, when I
asked him.

"Oh!" I exclaimed, sympathetically; "I am
so sorry."

I looked at him, and an idea occured to me.

"Stephen," said I, "when you and I grow big
enough, we will go on a pilgrimage to some monastery that has one of the teeth of St. Apolonia.
People say that her teeth cure the toothache.
And maybe, Stephen, you and I might be rich
enough to get one of St. Apolonia's teeth ourselves, and keep it always, and then we never
could have toothache any more, could we?   We
will keep the tooth where we both know where
it is, so that you can find it in a minute if I am
not home when your tooth begins to ache."

I grew quite enthusiastic over this plan, but to
Stephen, suffering from the present toothache, my
proposition of future help seemed to bring but
little relief.

"Why doesn't St. Apolonia help me now, if

she's ever going to?" sobbed Stephen, clasping his aching face; "I think she might. I think she isn't a real good saint if she doesn't help me now, when she knows I am going to a monastery to see her tooth as soon as I am big enough. Oh! Oh!"

And Stephen wept and would not be consoled, while I was quite shocked that Stephen did not speak more respectfully of St. Apolonia. For I believed in the magical power of that saint's teeth with all my heart.

Alas! It was not till years after, during the suppression of the monasteries, that I learned that the teeth of St. Apolonia, which had been held as sacred relics, had been brought together from the different convents, and it was found that there were so many of these teeth that they filled a tun; so wickedly had the monks deceived the poor English people by pretending that those were saints' teeth which were not.

"A goodly mouth had St. Apolonia," I heard a man laughingly say once in those after years, when he heard of the great quantity of teeth that had been collected. "Had ever a saint such a mouth as she to hold so many teeth?"

Ah, what a world was England, where men might believe as many such foolish superstitions as possible, and the priests would rejoice and foster such ideas; but let a man once go to the holy Scripture and read for himself, and strive to follow the solemn commands laid down there, and see with what fury the priests would rage. And if the simple reading of the word was such a sin in the eyes of Rome, what penalty would be sufficient punish the crime of those who not only dared to read the New Testament, but in spite of lash or fagot, would have courage to say that the priestly baptism received in infancy was nothing, and would be immersed on profession of their faith in Christ? Should an English person think for himself? Should he have an English New Testament? Should he dare be immersed? Not if Rome could prevent it. She had heard of these Anabaptists before. They had been thorns in her side. Rome had persecuted Anabaptists for centuries on centuries. Woe, woe to any in England who dared be "re-baptized."

Was it not enough that the sermons of John Huss had been full of " Anabaptistical errors " ; that the followers of Huss would admit none to their fellowship until such person was " dipped in water " ; that many of Huss' followers became Anabaptists? Had not Jerome of Prague been baptised by immersion, and were not Huss and Jerome both burned to death long ago? Had not Rome done her best to blot the Anabaptists from the earth? What was this doctrine that it should live and grow during all these centuries since the apostles' days?

CHAPTER IV

NEIGHBOR ELD RETURNS

NEIGHBOR ELD was back. 1528
I could hardly believe it when I met him A.D.
one morning on my journey from getting some
water. He knew me, and smiled at me as he
used to do. But he looked very thin and more
bent, and when his smile was gone his face was
more sad than I had ever seen it before. But how
many months he had been away.

"Oh!" I exclaimed joyfully; "I am so glad
you have come. I will tell father. Where have
you been?"

Neighbor Eld smiled again, but faintly, at the
childish heartiness of my greeting.

"I have been in London," he informed me.
And the sound of his voice was sad.

But I was too full of joy to notice sadness then,
and I ran toward home, carrying the water so care-
lessly that part of it spilled, so eager was I to tell
my mother that Neighbor Eld had returned.

My mother received the tidings calmly enough.

"So the priest did not find him at all, I think,"
I went on.

"What priest?" questioned my mother, to my
dismay, for I suddenly remembered that of course

35

I had never told her of the priest I had watched through the chink in the hut as he hunted for Neighbor Eld's Testament. My mother would have thought it dreadful that I should have set myself to be a spy on a priest. Now how should I explain to her without saying anything to betray Neighbor Eld's confidence?

But before I could collect my scattered wits enough to speak, my mother seized my dress and shook it a little.

"You have spilled water enough to wet your dress," she chided me. "You must be more careful."

Evidently she thought little of my words about the priest, and I ran away, thankful to escape observation, and determined to be more careful. I felt somewhat guilty at the thought of having any secret from my mother, however.

"But father knows. It is our secret about the New Testament," I argued, inwardly. "Father told me not to tell anybody. If mother knew about it, she might tell the priests. Father will be so glad to find out that Neighbor Eld has come. Now we shall hear the New Testament again."

So full was I of this thought that I paid but little heed to my cousin Stephen that evening, when he told me a friar had told him that day, that in one of the English monasteries there was to be seen the very ear which belonged to the servant Malchus, that was cut from his head by the sword of St. Peter.

"I am going to see that ear, when I am grown and can make pilgrimages," boasted Stephen.

But if I cared little for my cousin's speech, it was not so with a fierce, bigoted old woman, a neighbor of ours, who overheard Stephen, and patted him on the shoulder, and told him he was a good lad to think so much of religion.

"Pilgrimages are good, and the priests tell us to make as many as we can," quoth the stern old woman. "Laddie, never turn against the priests. They know religion. Those folk who turn against our religion shall have trouble. When I was as young as you, laddie, my mother told me once that St. Peter himself appeared one time, and punished even a priest who was going to neglect his duty to King Eadbald. You know, laddie, that King Eadbald ruled here hundreds of years ago, and he was a heathen king and married a widow, and was for turning away from our good religion that some bishops had tried to teach him. And two bishops that had been in this land preaching went back to France, but there was one left, named Laurentius. And he was about to go and leave the king to be a heathen. But the night before Laurentius was to go he had his bed made in the church. And in the morning he came to say good-bye, and showed his bare back and shoulders, all bloody with a whipping. And King Eadbald asked, 'Who has dared treat you so?' and Laurentius said, 'The prince of the apostles, St. Peter, came to me in the dead of night, and beat me because I had thought of leaving you and these people to be heathen persons.'

"And King Eadbald was so frightened at this sign from heaven that he put a stop to worshiping idols, and became a great Christian. And do you think if St. Peter punished a priest, he will not punish common folk who turn against the priests, and say they see no good in pilgrimages and holy relics, and wish, like that wicked man who, folks say has written the New Testament in English, to read the Scriptures themselves? You must never be wicked like that, laddie. It would be a great pity for a lad like you, living where you can go see our angel of the spear-head."

There were cold chills running up and down my back, and I was glad the fierce little old woman paid more attention to Stephen than to me. Her account of this one of the first Romish miracles of English history had frightened me, and I looked fearfully about as the shadows grew longer, dreading lest St. Peter should single me out also as a fit subject for punishment. He must know, I thought, that I had been with my father sometimes to Neighbor Eld's hut, and had seen a New Testament in English, and had even heard it read.

"Suppose," I whispered to myself, "oh, suppose St. Peter should come to me with a big whip in his hand!"

I was so frightened at this thought that I ran

into the house, and kept close beside my mother
for a while.

But still, when my father came tired with his
work, I made haste to tell him of old Neighbor
Eld's reappearance, and my father, I could see,
was very anxious to meet his friend.

"Let me go with you, father?" I pleaded softly
in his ear, my fears about St. Peter's wrath having vanished at his presence.   "Let me go?"

My father hesitated only a moment, ere he
replied, "Yes, child."

It was almost dark when we went quietly out
and hurried to Neighbor Eld's.

"He will read to us out of the New Testament
again," I whispered to my father.

"Hush!" he answered softly, and my few
words seemed to cause him such trepidation that
I wished I had not spoken.   Was it unsafe to refer
to the New Testament in any way?

My father rapped softly on Neighbor Eld's
door, but there was no answer.   Finally father
pushed the door open. The room inside was
nearly dark, but at last we perceived a bowed
form sitting near that place where the New Testament had formerly been hidden in the wall. We
stepped inside the hut, and sat down together
beside our old neighbor, but he paid no attention
to us.

"You have been gone long, good neighbor,"
began my father kindly.

But a great sob, as of recognition of us as

friends to whom some deep sorrow might be told, broke from old Neighbor Eld at these words, and my father, surprised and shocked, put his hand on the bowed form.

"Neighbor Eld," asked my father gently, "what troubles you?"

The old man could not speak, till at last, struggling with his sobs, he answered brokenly: "It is gone! It is gone!"

"The New Testament?" whispered my father.

Neighbor Eld made a sign of assent, and we sat in silence. This was indeed a heavy blow.

After a time, bending toward us, one hand supporting him, Neighbor Eld spoke:

"I opened my Testament that I might but see the holy words once again before I gave the book up to the fire," said the grieved old voice. "Poor, well-thumbed book, could not the cardinal's men have let me keep it? I shall never have another! *I shall never have another!*"

The old man sobbed the words over, as he rocked himself to and fro. My father sighed heavily. It seemed but too likely that Neighbor Eld would never have a New Testament again. So the priests had found him.

"Ah! but the book has been such a comfort to me," grieved the old man. "But what do you think the words were that I saw when I opened my Testament for the last time, just as I must give it up? 'He hath putt doune the myghty from their seates, and hath exalted them of lowe degre.' And a priest struck at the book in my hand, and the book fell into the fire, and I said in my heart : 'May God put down all such priests from their seats.' And I remembered the words that come before those I read : 'And hys mercy is always on them that feare him thorow oute all generacions.' "

Neighbor Eld's sobs were gone, and he appeared eager and excited.

" ' He hath putt doune the myghty from their seates, and hath exalted them of lowe degre," he repeated, as if he saw it already done.

We sat longer in the dark than we meant, for the old man told us of the imprisonment he had suffered for several months, and of the privations he had undergone. And then my father, saying that he had hungered for the words of the New Testament, begged the old man to tell anything that he remembered of the word.

And so for a long time Neighbor Eld's hushed voice went on repeating to us such passages of the Testament as he remembered, telling us other things partly in his own language and partly in the words of Scripture. My father listened eagerly as one whose soul thirsted for such tidings.

At last Neighbor Eld broke off suddenly, and we hastened to go, knowing that the weary old man ought to be sleeping.

"Tell no one of the loss of the New Testament, Editha," charged my father, on the way home.

I ventured to speak to my father of the fierce, little old woman's story of Laurentius' bloody back and shoulders, clinging very fast to his hand as I told him, and I cast a timid look behind us, while I asked: "Oh, father, do you think St. Peter would come and whip you and me to-night, for going to Neighbor Eld's to talk about the New Testament?"

My father stooped, and took me in his arms.

"No, Editha, no," he answered softly. "St. Peter will never harm you or me. Oh, my child, it is the Lord Jesus who has power over us. He loves us. His care is around you and me now. I wish your mother could understand how false all these monks' tales and priests' lies about the saints are. But I hope the Lord will lead her to see some day. Now it would grieve her to know that I pray no more to the saints or the Virgin. I pray only to the dear Lord who died for us, and I pray him to send a new heart and an open English Bible to every person in England. But love your mother and obey her, Editha, for she is right in all but this."

I did not wholly understand my father's speech; but I knew, as he gently put me down again and held my hand, that he cared very, very much about the New Testament and about the Lord Jesus, and was not at all afraid of St. Peter. I was very glad, and I looked boldly at the dark now since I was sure that St. Peter was not hiding in the shadows plotting vengeance.

"I will always tell father everything that
frightens me," I resolved. "He knows whether
I need be afraid or not. And I will never, never
tell anybody about the New Testament. I am
glad I have seen one, anyway."

But when we arrived home, the influences about
me changed somewhat. We found my mother
sprinkling a little holy water about my bed, and
I took this practice to be of course a part of religion. For my mother had always been wont to
sprinkle holy water about my bed and about her
own ; and my aunt at her house, sprinkled holy
water about her bed and about Stephen's, and my
mother and my aunt each used to carry a bit of
holy bread about with her, and made offerings of
candles, and believed much in rosaries, and in
many like things. And, moreover, my mother
knew, and often repeated certain prayers that
were to be said before the image of Our Lady of
Pity, which prayers would make sure, she believed,
that the person who said them should see Our
Lady's face, and "be warned both of the day and
hour of his death."

But my mother felt somewhat unhappy and
worried about my father, because last Good Friday
he had not crept to the cross, the omission of which
act was a heinous sin in her eyes. She of course
had crept to the cross on Good Friday, and had
made me do it too. My father had done it in past
years, but his actions now were incomprehensible
to my mother.

For as yet she knew nothing of my father's turning toward the Anabaptists, since he had not dared speak to her about that, but had begun to talk to me about it, his mind being so full of the subject that he could hardly refrain from speaking to some one. I tried to understand, thinking that my father shared wise thoughts with me, yet I hardly knew why he became so excited and earnest when he spoke of the matter. He told me, I remember, that the Anabaptists ought rightfully to be called Baptists, for they believed in but one baptism, but their enemies insisted on calling them "Anabaptists," and it could not be helped since there was no religious liberty in the land, and the priests were determined to bind every man's soul to the church of Rome.

"But the priests know well enough that the Anabaptists are older than the Catholics," my father went on eagerly. "Our belief about baptism goes back to the days of Christ's apostles, and is no new thing, as the priests would have people believe."

He sighed heavily, and I looked at him wondering and believing what was told me, and yet not realizing its grave import.

"I pray God that religious liberty may come to England sometime," broke forth my father, vehemently. "Remember, Editha, the Anabaptists are no new people, no matter what the priests may say."

"Religious liberty!" Whence had the Ana-

baptists that idea? Was it not from the New
Testament? Surely they never derived that idea
from two of the great leaders of the Reformation,
for neither Luther nor Zwingli was willing to
grant liberty of thought and action to the Anabaptists, though Luther and Zwingli themselves
demanded such liberty when disputing with the
Romanists. Why should one man demand religious liberty for himself, and deny it to another
man? Are we not all equal before God? So I
think that Luther, great and good man that he
was, did wrong in refusing liberty of conscience
to the Anabaptists; and I am sure that the Anabaptists derive their great idea of religious liberty
for all men from the New Testament.

CHAPTER V

NEIGHBOR ELD'S REWARD

THREE weeks' later I was doing an errand near nightfall. I hastened to be home, when suddenly a man stood before me in the way. He was a stranger, and though the twilight was deepening, I saw a very noticeable dark mark on one of his cheeks. I was startled by his unlooked-for coming, and would have run from him, but he spoke kindly.

"Did I fright you, little lass?" asked he. "Can you tell me where there lives a man called John Eld—an old man he is?"

I hastily gave directions for finding the house, and ran away, wondering at the dark mark on the man's face. I had a passing recollection of the stranger priest whom I had once directed to Neighbor Eld's house. But I was sure that this man was no priest. He looked more like a carpenter, or some hard-working man.

"I wonder what was the matter with his cheek?" I thought.

He would find Neighbor Eld at home I was sure, for the old man had grown so feeble that he seldom left his hut night or day. And whether the visitor were friend or foe, there would be no

46

New Testament to be found in Neighbor Eld's
hut.   But I heard no more of the man with the
marked cheek until the next night.

The evening of the next day my father came
home, and smiled at me as he said, "Editha,
when we have eaten, you and I will go and carry
some broth to Neighbor Eld.   We have been
together to see him only once since he came
back."

I was ready enough to go.   My mother made
the broth, and she and my aunt and Stephen had
hardly finished eating before my father and I set
forth on our errand.

But I was not prepared for the meeting between
my father and Neighbor Eld.   Into the little hut
my father and I went, I holding the broth.   But
I almost dropped it in my amazement when I saw
my father and Neighbor Eld, usually so undemon-
strative, throw their arms around one another, and
burst into tears !

There was a little silence, and then the old
neighbor's quivering voice murmured : "Blessed
be the Lord God of Israel, who has granted us his
word again."   And my father added, "Amen."

It was quite awhile before I could understand
what had occurred.   The stranger whom I had
directed to Neighbor Eld's hut the evening before
had been a bearer of good.   He was one of the
men who were secretly scattering the New Testament very widely throughout England.   He had
heard in some way of Neighbor Eld, and had

ventured into our town, daring the possible discovery by priests, in order to comfort the old man
with a Testament again. And so Neighbor Eld
had one now. I was so glad.

"There are a great many Testaments being
brought secretly into England," my father told
me, "and there are some London tradesmen and
citizens who have formed themselves into a company called the 'Christian Brethren,' and they
have sent out men to carry the Testaments here
and there secretly throughout the country, that
the poor may have the books."

But the bishop of London, Tunstall by name,
had issued an edict against the New Testament,
and men knew that the bishop would burn every
one of the books if he could, so English people
must beware.

It was hard for my father and for Neighbor
Eld to sufficiently quiet their excitement so that
they could read in the blessed book that had come
again. Neighbor Eld was weak, and it was difficult for him to see, and my father could not read
so well as the old man did, but between them
some precious words of Scripture were made out
and talked over. I listened with rapt attention,
trying to understand, for I had become aroused to
the idea that the New Testament must be a very
wonderful book, since people had to hide it so,
and make such a secret of owning a copy.

When we arose to go, Neighbor Eld nervously
asked my father if it would not be better for him

to take the New Testament with him for safe keeping.

"I am known to the friars as one whom they suspect," explained Neighbor Eld. "They know that I once had a Testament, and if they should find that one of the 'Christian Brethren' had been in this town, I might have a visit from the friars, and this Testament might be taken. But the priests do not suspect you, do they?"

My father hesitated.

"I know not," he answered. "Who can tell what secret ways the friars have of gaining knowledge of things?"

"Will you not take the Testament with you?" proffered the old man again. "It would be a sore loss to you as well as to me, if the priests should get the book."

The old man's voice trembled. He was offering to make a great sacrifice in letting my father take the book. But my father would not allow it.

"No, no," answered my father kindly. "The book will comfort you through the long days, and you can tell me what you have read."

"Come very often here then," replied Neighbor Eld. "Come and read the book. And, good friend, I have not many more days in this world. I know that. When I am dead the Testament is yours. You will find it in its place in the wall."

"Oh, Neighbor Eld, I hope you will live many years, even till the time comes when every man in England may have his own Bible, and read it

D

boldly," rejoined my father cheerily, and we went away.

"You must learn to read, Editha," my father said, as we walked home. "I will teach you the little I know, and I must learn all I can of Neighbor Eld. I must do it speedily, though I hope he may live long yet."

We walked on in silence a few minutes, and then my father spoke again.

"After you can read well, Editha," he continued, "you will be able to know what to believe, and what not to believe. Poor child! You have been told so many saints' tales, and have heard only a little of the Testament. I hardly know what a mixture of truth and error may be in your mind, but the New Testament is all true every word, and you must believe it all. But it troubles me to have you told such tales as that which your aunt told you and Stephen the other night."

I well remembered the story that my aunt had told us. It was one of the vain traditions of the friars concerning the rosary.

"St. Dominic," my aunt had said, in telling my cousin and myself the tale, "preached once in favor of the rosary, and a Spanish maiden hearing him, was convinced, and went and got herself a rosary, with which she told her beads quite regularly. Still she did not become better than she was before. But she used her rosary often enough. One day this maiden was seized, and her head was cut off and thrown into a well."

"Oh! oh!" Stephen and I exclaimed, greatly excited at such a catastrophe.

"Yes," affirmed my aunt, with great earnestness, "her head was cut off and thrown into a well ; and as she had sinned a great deal, she would have had a dreadful time if it had not been for that rosary. But because she had said her beads quite regularly, the Holy Virgin had pity on the maiden, and allowed her soul to come back into her head. Then St. Dominic received word about the girl, and he went to the well and said to the head, ' Come up.' "

Stephen's eyes and mine opened wide, and we listened breathlessly for the result of this command.

"Yes," nodded my aunt, enjoying our excitement, " St. Dominic said to the head, ' Come up,' and up the well the head came."

I gave a little gasp at this, and listened, awestruck.

" The head sat down on the well-side," continued my aunt, "and begged St. Dominic to help her. The girl's head said that she must pass two hundred years in purgatory unless St. Dominic and others would help her. And St. Dominic was so good and kind that he listened while the girl told him her sins, a thing she had not had time to do before her head had been cut off. And St. Dominic forgave her her sins, and she received the wafer. And for two days her head preached to the people who came to see her. And then she

died, and at the end of fifteen days her soul
appeared in glory to St. Dominic, and thanked
him for having, by the rosary, delivered her from
the place of penance.

"And so, children," concluded my aunt, "you
must always be sure to say your prayers over and
over and over, the more times the better, for the
rosary has great power, and you never can tell
what trouble even your prayers may save you
from."

I think if my father had heard all this tale, he
would have commanded my aunt never to tell me
any more saints' stories. But he had heard only
a few words of what she said to us, and so did not
interfere. He knew, in a general way, that she
spoke of one of the many, many legends con-
nected with the rosary, and perhaps with the
saints, legends that he wished I might not hear,
but which he could hardly prevent my knowing,
since my aunt and my mother both believed in
such tales to a great extent. The only thing that
had caused me to have any doubt of the wonderful
story at the time my aunt was speaking, was her
mention of purgatory. My father had distinctly
and repeatedly told me never to believe in such a
place, for he said it was not once mentioned in the
New Testament. But of course I dared not say
anything about the New Testament to my aunt.

She was displeased enough with my father
already because he had heard and learned some
rhymes that John Skelton, King Henry's rhymster,

had written about the priests and the bishops. The rhymes were very bold indeed, and told of the bad doings of the clergy, and my father had repeated some of the words before my aunt at home one evening, and had thereby gained her strong disapproval.

"He says," my father told us on that evening, speaking of John Skelton, "because the priests are so very ignorant—

> " A priest without a letter,
> Without his virtue be greater,
> Doubtless were much better
> Upon him for to take
> A mattocke or a rake."

Even I, child that I was, had cried out at the audacity of that last sentence.

"Why, father," I cried; "no priest would work the way you do, with a plough or a rake!"

My father's face was stern.

"No," he answered, "they are much too idle for that."

And then I think my mother must have softly reminded him that I was but a little lass to hear such things, for my father's face changed afterward, and he bade me not to trouble my small head about John Skelton's rhymes.

It was only a few weeks after Neighbor Eld had obtained the copy of the New Testament which gave us such joy, that the old man became very much more feeble. His strength, which had

seemed little enough since his return, now gave
way so that he could hardly prepare his own simple meals. My father charged me to sometimes
look in during the days and see how the old man
fared, and at last I always carried him his supper,
and waited there till my father came.

Neighbor Eld usually greeted me when I
entered, but one evening I went in and found him
lying on his straw asleep. I stepped lightly not to
waken him. He lay still, breathing heavily, very
heavily indeed it seemed to me.

"But perhaps he always does so when he is
asleep," I reflected, and kept very quiet, resolving
not to disturb him.

"I wish father would come," I thought, as
Neighbor Eld's breathing grew more and more
loud. "Perhaps if I should touch his hand he
might waken a little and not breathe quite so
hard. It frightens me."

For the hoarse breathing made a great deal of
noise now, it seemed to me, in the quiet hut. But
I dared not go near enough to the straw bed to
touch the old man and waken him. Someway I
was afraid. I shrank back into the corner near
the opening which I had peered through the day
when I looked at the doings of the priest inside
the little hut. I listened to Neighbor Eld's
breathing. By-and-by it grew less loud. It became less and less. I waited, and the quiet room
held no sound that I could perceive from the
place where I sat.

It had been so for a long time when the door opened and my father came in.

"How is he, Editha?" he asked, softly.

"He is asleep," I answered cautiously. "He breathed very loudly for a while, but he is still now."

My father went over to the straw. He knelt down silently. Then he put his hand suddenly on the old man's head.

"Neighbor Eld!" exclaimed my father, in a startled way.

There was no answering sound.

"Neighbor Eld," repeated my father.

But there was silence, a silence that would never be broken by the old man's voice. My father lifted Neighbor Eld's head, and sent me for water, and tried in every way to bring back some sign of life, but the closed eyes did not open, and the forehead was cold. Neighbor Eld looked as if he were asleep.

"He will never waken, Editha," my father pronounced sentence at last. "Let us call in the neighbors."

"Is he dead?" I asked, and my father answered, "Yes."

A few of the neighbors came at our summons, and one of the women said I ought to have shaken the old man when he breathed so strangely, and perhaps I might have wakened him, and he might have recovered. But my father told me afterward that I was not to blame. I had not known what to do, and nothing could have saved the old man from dying.

"He was ready to die," added my father; "and if you and I have the Lord Jesus forgive us our sins, Editha, and try to follow him, we shall see Neighbor Eld again some day. I thank God that he is out of the power of the priests."

But I was overwhelmed with grief at the loss of my old friend. We had gone to see him so often, and he had always been so kind to me, telling me stories from the New Testament and helping me learn to read.

It was only the evening before this that my father and I had been with Neighbor Eld, and the old man had said to me, "Read a little out of the New Testament, Editha," and I had been very proud to do so, to show that I was beginning to know how to read somewhat better.

Neighbor Eld found the place in the New Testament. "Read here," he said, pointing.

And I read the words: "Oure Father which arte in heven, halowed be thy name. Let thy kingdom come. Thy wyll be fulfilled, as well in erth, as hit ys in heven. Geve us this daye oure dayly breade. And forgeve vs oure treaspases, even as we forgeve them which treaspas vs. Leede vs not into temptacion, but delyvre vs from yvell. Amen."

But Neighbor Eld would never read in his New Testament again. He would never hear me read any more. I cried when I thought of it.

The New Testament was my father's now, since Neighbor Eld had left it to him, and my father took the book secretly away when we left the hut that night. I wondered very much where father would keep the New Testament so that mother should not find it.

But my mother had no thought of such a book being in the house. What she inquired very anxiously of me was whether Neighbor Eld had spoken anything to me about mass being said for his soul after death.

"No," I answered, and my mother looked frightened.

"I wish he had," she murmured.

The priests were very strict about folks who died, and if such had left no wish that masses should be said for their souls after death, it was considered a proof that the dead person had been a heretic. In such cases the priests were very severe.

But in our town of Caversham, old Neighbor Eld was allowed to be peaceably buried, though I have always thought it was because my mother and my aunt were kind-hearted enough to pay the priests something not to interpose any authority to prevent our old neighbor's quiet burial.

Yet, if the priests had known what my father knew, I cannot tell what amount of money it might have taken to assuage their wrath, or whether indeed money would have had power to do it. But my father kept his secret well, and it

was not till months after Neighbor Eld's funeral
that my mother knew that the old man had been
one of those Christians called Anabaptists, and
that he and my father had many a time talked of
immersion as taught in the New Testament, and
had spoken together of the persecutions that Anabaptists have endured through the ages, yea, and
were yet to endure, judging from all indications.

And yet I think if my father could have looked
forward to that day when King Henry VIII.
would send to convocation the article saying that
baptism is "necessary to salvation"; that infants
were "to be baptized for the pardon of original
sin"; and that the opinions of the Anabaptists
are "detestable heresies"; if my father could
have looked forward to that other day when sixteen men and fifteen women were banished from
England for opposing infant baptism, and afterward going to Delft in the Low Countries, were
persecuted and put to death as Anabaptists, the
men being beheaded and the women drowned;
if my father could have looked forward to old
Bishop Latimer's declaration that "Anabaptists
were burned in different parts of the kingdom,
and went to the stake with good integrity," I
still think that my father would not have gone
back from that which he believed the New Testament teaches, the immersion of those only who
have faith in our Lord Jesus Christ as their
Saviour from sin.

And yet it is well that we cannot look forward

For you can see that at this time my father had but recently emerged from the darkness of the Popish faith, and perhaps he might have been affrighted if he could have foreseen the dreadful days in store for Anabaptists, not only in England, but in the country whither we went. But God leads us on as we are able to bear it, and his strength is promised to us in accordance with our days. It has been only by his grace that any Anabaptist has stood firm, for truly all the powers of intolerance seem to have opposed themselves to the people of the Anabaptist faith.

And, as it has been in this way in many ages, perhaps this fact has had its effect in making our Anabaptist folk such champions of religious liberty as we have ever been. Though religious liberty is most truly an idea of God's holy word, and it must be that Anabaptists first found the thought in that book, for I am sure they could not have found the idea in any country on earth. But there are certain ideas of God's word that came, through our personal experiences, to be most firmly impressed upon us, and I think, through the oppression and persecution which we Anabaptists have received, this thought of religious freedom has laid hold on us, and so fired us with zeal that we have struggled more than other people to make the idea a reality.

CHAPTER VI

COUNTING THE COST

NIMBLE-TONGUED and indignant Dame Burnet stood in the doorway talking to my mother.

"They have found it out now. They have found it out," declared our voluble neighbor. "Who would suppose that for a year and a half those New Testaments could be passing from hand to hand secretly ; and the bishop of London, poor man, he having all his spies and informers hunting, and yet never find out till now how the books have been scattered. Such a trial as it must have been to the bishop. It's the 'Christian brethren' that have been doing all the mischief. They have been sly, but they have been found out now. Farmers, peasants, tradesmen they are, even some priests doing such a thing as helping the New Testament around the country. But it is well found out. Crowds of country folk are being dragged in now, put in prison, or sent before the bishop's court. The bishops will see that there are no more Testaments handed around."

"It is terribly wicked to have a book like that in the house," sighed my mother, shaking her head, as Dame Burnet paused for breath.

"Wicked!" shrieked Dame Burnet. "Why, all England seems to be going wicked. Some one was telling me that all Essex seems to have gone over to the New Testament, and in London the books are for sale. But the people are getting scared. They will have to give up those books or go to prison or be burned. Something will happen, now that the bishop of London has found out what he wanted to know."

My mother moved a little uneasily. She was much more kind-hearted than Dame Burnet.

"I hope the bishops will not have to burn anybody," my mother answered, hesitatingly. "They ought to burn the New Testaments of course, but——"

She was interrupted by a scornful laugh.

"Nothing is too bad for such folks," asserted Dame Burnet. "I was in London seven years ago, in 1521, when the heretics were punished there. Even when they recanted, there was a time. Many are the heretics I have seen made to go three times around the market on market day, stand on the highest step of the cross there for a quarter of an hour with a fagot of wood on their shoulder; and they had to go in the same way in a procession on Sunday; and they were branded with a red-hot iron on the cheek; and they must never in any way hide the mark."

My mother shivered.

"Something had to be done," expostulated Dame Burnet, noting the effect of her words.

"Bishop Longland hunted up in that year nearly five hundred Gospellers. They used to do such awful things, those Gospellers! They would teach children Bible verses, and they would say the Ten Commandments,—which I never knew, and never will,—and they said, 'What need is there to go to the feet when we may go to the head?'—meaning the priests by 'the feet,' mind you, and the Bible or some such thing, by 'the head.' And they would carry their books from one man to another, and read all night sometimes in a book, and some of them would eat on a fast-day, and they would never go on any pilgrimage, for they said the true pilgrimage was 'to go bare-foot and visit the poor and sick,'—and much good it would do anybody to have such visitors."

My mother smiled. Dame Burnet was never herself so very welcome a visitor at our house, though my mother was ever kind and friendly.

"And," pursued Dame Burnet, "those Gos-pellers had pieces of the old Wycliffe English Bible, that almost no one could read and no one ought to, and they would not give the pieces up, or worship the Virgin and the saints; but the Gospellers said, 'Blessed be they that hear the word of God and keep it.' Well, they got what they deserved! The bishop had the Gospellers torn out of their houses, and either burnt to death or else, if they recanted, they had to wear the fagot badge for life. Many is the one I had seen walking the street with the fagot badge on his clothes, and the mark of the burn of the iron on his cheek. And if the wicked heretics now don't give up their New Testaments, we would like to see the same again."

The women paid no attention to me. They did not know that there swept before me a vision of the man I had directed to Neighbor Eld's hut. The man's cheek had a queer, dark mark.

"That was it," I thought. "He must have been burned once on his cheek, because he was a Gospeller. How it must have hurt. And he brought Neighbor Eld the Testament."

My very heart was quaking within me. What did burning people to death mean? What would my mother say if she knew that father had a New Testament? A priest found out about Neighbor Eld's first Testament. Could not some priest find out about my father's Testament too? And my father was an Anabaptist.

"There are a good many of the butchers and tailors and carpenters among those 'Christian Brethren,' who know they are suspected, and they are trying to get out of England," declared Dame Burnet, as she made ready to go. "They are trying to hide in the holds of ships, or else they are fixing themselves up so they think no one will know them. But they will not be a bit better off over in France or Belgium, for English folk can go over there and arrest them."

Dame Burnet went away, but my spirits were made more dismal still by my aunt, Stephen's

mother, who said she recollected that nine years
ago, six men and a woman were burned at Coventry, because they had taught their children and
their servants the Lord's Prayer, the Creed, and
the Ten Commandments in English.

Alas! I myself remembered enough of the
New Testament to repeat under my breath sometimes the Lord's Prayer in English. It seemed so
pleasant to say words that I could understand, instead of praying in Latin. I was always terribly
afraid though, that to punish me the saints would
make me forget the Latin words, and my mother
would find it out, and be shocked by my sudden
ignorance.

But I wondered that the saints and the Virgin
would not just as lief hear me pray in English as
in Latin. Was Latin so holy a language? Or
perhaps the saints did not understand English?

People who taught their children the Lord's
Prayer in English, had been burned. Did that
mean that my father would be? He was an Anabaptist too. Was that worse? I was so frightened
that I burst into tears, and my aunt vainly tried
to comfort me, blaming herself meanwhile for
having spoken of such things. But I cried on and
on till my mother in alarm declared that she believed I was ill.

Oh, if I only dared tell my mother what ailed
me! But I must never, never speak of the New
Testament.

"What is the matter?" queried my mother.

And at last I sobbed, "Oh, father, father! I am so afraid that something will happen to father."

My mother laughed a little, as she drew my head closely to her.

"Editha, Editha," she chided, gently. "Nothing will happen to father. Silly little lass. Dame Burnet must not talk about things before you any more. I did not think you would feel so, Editha." And my mother patted my cheek, and kissed me, and then she went away, and cut a piece of cheese, and gave half to Stephen and half to me.

This was a very great treat, and Stephen and I rejoiced over our dainty. But I could not be very merry, though I had cried away much of my terror. I resolved that I would beg my father that very night to dig a hole in the ground, and hide the New Testament instead of keeping it where it might be found. I looked about for a good place to dig the hole.

"Let us go to see the angel," proposed Stephen, who of course did not know of what I was thinking.

I shook my head.

"You go," I answered.

I was glad enough to have him take a fancy to visit our one-winged friend.

"When Stephen is gone I will dig the hole, and have it ready before father comes," I determined.

But Stephen refused to go without me, and he lingered near till I found that I could do nothing

E

about the hole but select with my eye what I thought would be a good spot among some weeds near our house.

I clenched my small fists at the idea of any one daring to lay hold on my father and burn a great red place on his cheek, because he had a New Testament.

" He *shall* have a New Testament if he wants it," I resolved, angrily. "Whatever he wants is right. And if—if they do burn his cheek "—my courage was becoming faint again—" if they do burn his cheek, I will always love him, always, no matter how ugly the burn makes him look."

And I felt like crying again, only I diverted myself by thinking how I would hide my father's New Testament for him, and never tell, no matter what happened. Oh, I would be very wonderfully brave indeed.

But I found no opportunity that evening to say anything to my father about my plan of the hole, and the next day something happened that I had hardly expected.

It was Sunday. It had been my father's custom some times on Sundays to walk with me to some quiet place in the fields, and there read the New Testament and talk with me about what we read. And my father would there pray with me that the Lord Jesus might take away my sins.

But this afternoon my father stayed at home. My cousin Stephen was over at my aunt's house of course with his mother, and I slipped outdoors

alone, leaving my father and my mother together.
After a short time I went into the house again,
and I was surprised to see that my father was
reading the New Testament. My mother was
sitting not far off, and she was crying silently. I
went to her, and would have comforted her, but
my father came too and put his arms around us
both. We were very still, except that my mother
sobbed once or twice. My father answered my
inquiring look.

" Yes, Editha," he said softly ; " mother knows
about the New Testament. I told her last night
after you were asleep. I thought it was time that
mother knew."

My mother knew, and my mother was afraid.
Or else why did she cry so?

But oh, I was so glad that she knew. It had
been so hard to have to keep a secret from one's
own mother.

" Oh, father," I burst forth ; " do hide the New
Testament in a hole. I will help you dig."

My father looked at me.

" Editha," he replied, " do not speak about the
New Testament before Stephen or your aunt.
We three, you and mother and I, may talk of it to
one another all we please, quietly. Let us read to
mother, you and I, Editha."

And my mother, though apparently terrified at
what she was doing, listened to me as I read somewhat stumblingly. And then my father read to
us. His voice was calm and soothing, and my

mother stopped crying and listened with a good deal of interest after a while. She even asked a few questions about what he read.

At last she asked, as one who had made up her mind to accept the worst : "Are you going to be one of the ' Christian Brethren ' ? "

My father hesitated.

" I am one with them in loving the New Testament already, dear lass," he answered, slowly ; " but there is another matter that Neighbor Eld and I have often talked of. If I do as I think this New Testament bids, I shall be more than one of the ' Christian Brethren.' "

My mother was silent, but she looked fixedly at him. He smiled tenderly, but his eyes filled with tears.

" I have read this New Testament from end to end times over," he went on, "and neither Neighbor Eld nor I could find in it anything about praying to the saints, or about purgatory, or about praying for the dead. So I knew I must cut loose from the priests."

My father stopped a moment, but my mother still said nothing.

" Neighbor Eld believed that he did not find something else in the New Testament," continued my father. "And indeed I cannot find it there myself ; and that is the way the priests do baptize us when we are babies, and bring us afterward into the church, and so there is first no change of heart in us. For the New Testament tells us

plainly to repent and be baptized, and Neighbor
Eld said to me that a wee baby cannot repent, and
that is true enough. The reason why Neighbor
Eld was first thinking about that was this: When
he was a boy, his grandfather lived in Oxford, and
he used to tell him about some men and women
that were whipped through Oxford streets years
ago. There were about thirty of them, and they
called themselves 'Publicans,' which was probably
a corruption of the term 'Paulicians.' They had
come over to England from Gascony, and they
had with them a pastor named Gerard.

"Henry II. was King of England then, and he
heard about these Publicans that the priests
were all against, but King Henry was so just
he would not let the poor people be punished
without a hearing. And so there came together
a council of popish bishops of Oxford to try these
men and women. The pastor, Gerard, spoke
for them. He told the bishops that he and his
company were Christians and that they held the
doctrines of the apostles. But when the bishops
asked more questions, it was found that the Publicans did not believe in purgatory, or in prayers
for the dead, or in praying to saints, or in the baptism of babies, or in the changing of the bread
and wine of the sacrament into the body and
blood of Christ.

" The bishops tried to argue, but they could do
nothing with their words, for the Publicans
would not admit anything contrary to the word

of God, though they were only poor peasants.
The bishops were so angry that they reported to
King Henry that the Publicans were obstinate
heretics, worthy of death. And King Henry was so
influenced by the priests that he sentenced all the
Publicans to be branded with a red-hot iron on
their foreheads, as heretics; to be publicly
whipped through the streets of Oxford; and afterward to be put to death. And nobody should
show the Publicans any kindness or comfort, for
he who did would be punished."

There was indignation in my mother's face, but
still she said nothing.

"It was done this way," continued my father,
with a sigh. "Their foreheads were burnt; the
minister had a mark burnt on his chin as well as
his forehead; the Publicans were driven out of
the city with loud sounding stripes and the
hedges and fields were covered with snow, as it
was winter then, and the men, and women, and
children of the Publicans all died in the fields
of cold and hunger, for no one showed them any
kindness."

My mother drew a long breath.

"It was cruel!" she murmured.

"The Publicans rejoiced as they went out to
die," concluded my father, in a low tone. "The
pastor, Gerard, went before them, singing some
words that Neighbor Eld found for me in the New
Testament. They are 'Blessed are ye when all
men shall hate you.'"

There was a long pause.

"Oh, I wish," broke out my father vehemently, " I wish the time might ever come when every man in England might worship God as he thought right! Freedom! Freedom! That is what we want! Freedom to pray to God and worship him and read our New Testaments as he has commanded us!"

My father arose excitedly. He started to leave the house, when my mother stopped him.

" You did not tell us," she reminded him, " why it was you told us about the Publicans. Was Neighbor Eld one? Are you one?"

Her eyes looked at him as though she would read his soul. My father returned her gaze with equal solemnity. He knew what a heart-wrench his words must give her.

" They are not called Publicans now," he replied. " They are called Anabaptists. Neighbor Eld was one. I am one in my belief, though I have never yet been baptized as the New Testament tells me to be, and as I yet hope to be."

" But it is dangerous to read the New Testament," expostulated my mother, her voice trembling.

"Yes," agreed my father. "More than a hundred years ago, under King Henry IV., after John Wycliffe had been dead many years, the clergy came together and made a law that 'the translation of the text of Holy Scripture out of one tongue into another is a dangerous thing.

Therefore,' said they, ' we decree and ordain that no one henceforth do, by his own authority, translate any text of the Holy Scriptures into the English tongue.' The clergy said though, that translations might be read if they were approved by the bishops or by a council. But no such translations have ever been approved in all these years ! It is no new thing that the priests should hate to let us common folk have the Holy Scripture. But we must have it ! A man's conscience has a right to be free ! "

My mother was not a woman to oppose her husband, deeply as she had been shocked to find a New Testament in our home. She had too long been accustomed to submission to others in religious matters to rise in defiance now, and declare that the dreaded New Testament must not be allowed in the house.

I could readily see that it would have been a great relief to her to have burned the book, but my father's will was her law, and, much as she might grieve, many prayers as she might make to the saints about this matter, she would keep the possession of the book a secret, even though she thought she endangered her soul by not confessing this thing to the priests. My mother would have gone to the stake with my father, but at this time it would have been for love of him, not for love of the New Testament or of the Lord Jesus.

I noticed how my mother would shrink after

this, every time that my aunt spoke of those who read the New Testament.

"Such people are very stubborn, I have heard," asserted my aunt, one day; "but sometimes a good many of them come back to their senses, and recant, and obey the priests again! I remember there was a year, a good while ago, when I was a girl, that the folk called the year of the great abjuration, because so many heretics recanted. Perhaps such a year will come again."

My mother answered nothing, and I was sure that in her heart she did not believe that my father would ever recant. He had too well counted the cost of defying the priests before he ever told my mother of his change in belief. He would never go back to the priests and friars, no matter what might come to pass.

After the Sunday when we first read the New Testament to my mother, my father daily read a little to us at home. It seems to me but a short time after this, as I look back, and yet I know it must have been in the autumn of the next year, that the Bishop of London, Bishop Tunstall, returned from a mission to Cambray, and brought with him all of the New Testaments that he had been able to buy in Antwerp. Bishop Tunstall made a great bonfire of the New Testaments at Cheapside.

Of course this was exciting to the English people, but it was a foolish thing to do, for the money that Bishop Tunstall had paid for the New Testaments went another way from which he would like. The money went to pay for printing a new edition of the New Testament, and thousands of corrected copies were secretly brought into England very soon. But I run on before my story.

" Do you think," my mother asked my aunt one day, " if a person paid the priests a great deal of money, that they would let a heretic alone ? "

My aunt promptly shook her head

" No," she answered. " Have you forgotten how years ago there was a a rich man, Robert Bartlet, who had to lose his farm and his goods, and he was kept a prisoner in the monastery of Ashrigg for seven years, with a badge upon his right sleeve ? "

"Yes," responded my mother slowly, "I remember."

But while the priests did all they could against those whom the Romish clergy called heretics, some of the good people across the sea in the Low Countries had a scheme of their own for introducing the New Testament more widely into England. About Christmas time, 1528, this scheme was working beautifully. New Testaments, hidden in loads of corn, an eatable very much needed in England just then, came to our country. A bookseller of Antwerp, named John Raimond, had printed a fourth edition of the New Testament, more beautiful, my father said, than the former Testaments, for this kind had pictures, and each page was bordered with red lines.

The sacks of corn, with New Testaments inside them, passed bravely on ; but alas! certain priests and monks, always prying around, discovered that the sacks were not all corn ! The priests forthwith carried several copies of this New Testament to the bishop of London. Now the bookseller, John Raimond, instead of staying home in Antwerp, had come over to England on board one of the ships with five hundred copies of his New Testament, and when the bishop of London heard what the priests had to say, he laid hands on Raimond, and threw him into prison. But the bishop could not get many of the pretty, red-lined New Testaments. They went everywhere, and the New Testament was explained in frequent conventicles in the city of London, and the priests were so disgusted that they said : " It is sufficient only to enter London to become a heretic ! "

No wonder that in the autumn of 1529, Bishop Tunstall took all the English New Testaments that he had been able to buy in Antwerp, and made his great bonfire ! A pretty amusement that was for a bishop ! But such bonfires would light in men's hearts a fire that would not be put out.

My father still read his New Testament. Wonderful words he found there, and much reasoning went on in his mind. One day when I found him reading, he put his arm about me, and read a few words more, and then he said to me : " Ah, Elitha, I have not done all that the Lord commands me ! This word says, ' Repent, and be baptized.' I have repented, but I have not been baptized."

"Not when you were a baby, father?" I asked, in surprise. "Why, I was."

"'Therefore are we buried with him,'" murmured my father. "Jesus went *up out of* the water. It is not a drop of holy water on one's forehead, but a burial. Neighbor Eld and I used to talk of it often. He made it so plain."

My father stopped. Then he seemed to remember my question.

"When I was a baby?" he repeated. "When I was so small that I did not know how to repent? Yes, I was handed to the priest, but the New Testament says 'repent' comes first. That is what Neighbor Eld used to say, and it is true enough. And Tyndale, the man who wrote out the New Testament in English, says, 'The plunging into the water signifieth that we die and are buried with Christ; and the pulling out again signifieth that we rise again with Christ in a new life.' Did I do that when I was a baby, baptized by the priest, Editha? Was my life different after baptism? I had not repented; I was too little to believe. Why should the priest have baptized me? Why should I count that baptism as aught now?"

I could not answer. I was puzzled by his words.

"Editha," continued my father gently, "has mother said to you that she wished I would not become an Anabaptist?"

The tears were in his eyes.

"No," I answered, "no. She has not said so to me."

For my mother would never have spoken so of my father to me. But I silently remembered that last Ash-Wednesday father had not gone to have any ashes cast upon him, and afterward my aunt had said something to my mother about my father's absence, and my mother had cried. I knew, though she did not say so, that my mother wished my father had been among those people whom the priest absolved, and on whom he afterward cast ashes. My father was becoming a marked man.

CHAPTER VII

THE FAGOT RETREAT

1529 A.D. "I WONDER how much money mother will get to-morrow," I said to Stephen. "To-morrow is Hoke-day."

"Tuesday is Hoke-day," disputed Stephen.

"Tuesday for the men, but to-morrow for the women," I corrected him. "I wonder how much money mother will get to-morrow!"

"The priests will want her to get a great deal," answered Stephen.

It was two weeks after Easter, and it was the custom that when Hoke-tide came, the women would take cords, and go out into the streets and roads and stop all the men who passed, and bind them with the cords, not loosing such prisoners till they had paid a little amount of money. The men, on another day would take cords and treat the women in the same way.

It was rude sport, but the money gained in this way was given to the priests as an offering to the church. There was a supper, and Stephen and I liked the merriment. But my father, who grew, it seemed, daily more uneasy under the rule of the priests had said lately that he could wish that my mother would not raise any money in this way

on Hoke-day.   But my mother laughed lightly at
his misgivings and warned him that if he were
not brisk this Hoke-tide, she would be more successful than he in getting money.   My father
smiled at her merry tone, though his eyes looked
distressed.

My father did not intend to raise any money for
the priests this Hoke-tide.   I think my mother
knew that very well.   She spoke light-heartedly
enough, but she was really in dread of what the
priests would say, and she strove to make up by
her own unusual zeal the lack of interest that
my father showed.   She hoped to ward off the
displeasure of the priests for a time longer.   And
yet I believe she felt a thrill of terror, thinking
that she could not always continue to shield her
husband.   But she did help the other women get
much money for the priests that Hoke-tide.

It was a number of months after this when my
father became aware that the priests strongly suspected him.   It was little wonder, for my father
had absented himself from service, not going to
matins, or mass, or vespers, and nevermore making confession to the priest.   No marvel that fierce
eyes were on my father and mischief was plotted
against him.

"I must go into hiding," I overheard my
father tell my mother one night, after I was in
bed.

My aunt and Stephen were gone away at this
time on a pilgrimage with some others to see the

relics at the shrine of Reading, and I think my
father thought that he would do better to hide
while she was away, so that if necessary his place
of concealment might be a secret to her even—
for my aunt was more obedient to the priests and
more under their control than my mother, and
though my aunt liked my father very well, yet
there was no telling whether if he were hiding,
and she knew the place where he was hidden, and
a priest should command her to tell where it was,
she might not obey.   My aunt had been zealous
over her pilgrimage and had urged us to go too,
for over at Reading people said there were many,
many relics, bits of the arms of St. Pancrates, St.
Quentin, St. David, Mary Salome, and St. Edward the Martyr, and a bone of Mary Magdalene.

"I must go into hiding," repeated my father.
"The priests suspect me."

"Oh, Ralph," begged my mother; "give up
the Testament.   It will lead you into trouble.   It
has led so many to death !   The priests will never
stop hunting you, if once they really begin.
Give up the New Testament!   Think of Editha.
Think of me.   How can we live without you?
The priests will kill you !   I hear dreadful things
from the neighbor folk of how matters go elsewhere.   I am afraid for you all the time.   Let
me burn the book, and do you go to church and
to confession as you used to.   Do not be an Anabaptist.   Oh, do not!   I am afraid for you !"

She wept softly and he tried to soothe her.

"You were not shriven at Shrove-tide," she sobbed. "If you had only gone to the priest then, penance might have saved you. Oh, Ralph, I have prayed so much to the saints for you!"

She tried to check her sobs.

"Poor little wife! Poor, mistaken little wife!" murmured my father brokenly. "If you only knew ——"

"Even now," urged my mother, "if you should go to the priest and confess everything, he would forgive you, if you did penance. I am sure he would! Will you not go, Ralph?"

I listened to hear what my father would reply. Perhaps I ought not to have listened, but child though I was, I had heard Neighbor Eld and my father discuss the church of Rome enough so that I know my father could never be an honest Papist again as he had once been.

There was a long silence till my father spoke, his voice yet trembling.

"I have confessed my sins to God," replied my father, "and I have absolution through Jesus Christ our Lord."

I could hear my mother sobbing and pleading for a long while and my father answering her kindly, and yet I knew that he had not changed his decision.

By-and-by father came softly to my bed, and knelt down and kissed me gently, as if he was afraid of waking me. But I was wide awake, and I put my arms around his neck, and he said:

F

"Good night, Editha. Father is going to hide
in the big fagot pile, and you must not tell anybody where he is."

"Are you going to take the Testament?" I
questioned, trying to see his face in the dark.

"Yes," he answered, "I have it. Good-bye,
Editha."

And then he almost sobbed, as he murmured:
"Oh, Editha, Editha! May I live to see a Testament in every home in England, and all the wee
ones, like my own little girl, free to read it!"

He kissed me again and went away.

There was a great quantity of fagots heaped up,
a little back of our house, and during the night
my father constructed a kind of hollow hiding-
place inside the large pile. In this place he hid,
having taken with him some food and clothes,
together with the New Testament.

After this, sometimes by night I would climb
the pile of fagots and hide in the big hole with
father, whispering to him all the news I could
remember. He had fixed the fagots over his
head so that his hiding place was quite well concealed.

Once in the daytime I was near the large
pile getting a few fagots for mother to burn,
when suddenly one of our priests appeared near
me.

"Did your father go with your aunt and the
others on the pilgrimage to the Gray Friars at
Reading?" he asked.

And when I tremblingly answered "No," the priest looked sternly at me, and hesitated.

"He went *not* on that pilgrimage?" questioned the priest, transfixing me with his piercing gaze. "But he is not at home. I have not seen him in the village. He went *not* on that pilgrimage?"

"No," I said, trembling so with fear that I could hardly keep from bursting into tears.

Then the priest went away as swiftly as he had come.

I had expected that he would climb the big fagot pile and find father. I knew better than to climb the fagot pile myself in the daytime, even though the priest had disappeared, but I dropped my two fagots and ran into the house and told mother what had happened.

After this my father began to think that perhaps we might try to escape from England, as so many other folks were attempting to do, but we hardly knew how to accomplish it, and we knew that King Henry could send and take us, even if we fled from his realm.

"Oh," I thought, "I wish we could fly as well as the one-winged angel did. Then we could fly safely out of England some night, and father could carry his Testament with him, and no one would ever know where we went."

This exceedingly impossible childish wish exercised my imagination a great deal, but was of no practical avail.

It was in this year that King Henry published

a proclamation against the "Gospelers," with a
list of English books that were forbidden. When
my father heard of it, he repeated something that
William Tyndale said once about perceiving by
experience "how that it was impossible to establish the lay people in any truth except the Scriptures were plainly laid before their eyes in their
mother-tongue."

My aunt and Stephen came back from their
pilgrimage, and in my hearing my aunt said not
a word about my father's disappearance. My
mother must have said something to my aunt, but
I did not know what. If Stephen had been like
some boys, I should have been afraid of his finding out about father's being in the fagot heap.
But Stephen was not a boy to do much discover-
ing. He was a very dreamy sort of a person, and
would rather watch pilgrims come to and go from
the shrine of our town, and listen to the tales
they told, and note the wonder at our one-winged
angel, than be prying around our fagot pile.

Stephen was much delighted with the pilgrimage that he and his mother had made to Reading,
and he told me of having seen the monument of
the first King Henry, at the abbey of that place.

"A woman pilgrim there told me a story,"
Stephen informed me. "She said there used to be
a man that the first King Henry made a prisoner,
and the king was angry because the man had
written some verses that laughed at the king.
And King Henry was so wicked that he said the

man's eyes must be put out ; and when they were doing it, it hurt so that the man hit his head against the prison wall and it killed him. Cousin Editha, would our King Henry put out a man's eyes?"

"I don't know," I answered, remembering some of the dreadful things that Dame Burnet had mentioned.

But Stephen had already turned to another idea.

"Cousin Editha," he asked, "don't the saints want their arms any more?"

"I don't know," I repeated.

"There were so many arms of the saints at the Gray Friars," went on Stephen ; "I suppose the saints left their arms there for the friars to take care of."

I said nothing. I was a little envious that Stephen should have seen so much more than I had. But I reflected that at least Stephen had never seen a New Testament, and I had, although I dared not boast of that to Stephen, to offset his tales of what he had seen on his pilgrimage. I reflected, furthermore, that I knew about the Anabaptists, and Stephen did not know. I was certainly a great deal wiser than he about them, for my father had told me all he knew about the persecutions the Anabaptists had endured, and how such people loved and read the New Testament, and believed that no king has a right to take God's word from the common classes of men

who need it so much. But I sighed as I thought
that I must keep silent about all my knowledge,
and so had nothing wise wherewith to amaze
Stephen. Though he would have been amazed
indeed, if he had known what my father said to
me one night in the fagot hole, when he had been
telling me what the Anabaptists had endured in
the past in our country and in other lands.

"Editha," whispered my father, "the Anabaptists have had a glorious history in the past.
They will have a glorious history in the future.
Oh, my child! shall not you and I be worthy of that
history? Shall we not do our part in the struggle
for religious freedom? It will come some day,
Editha, this freedom we Anabaptists want for all
men. Then no man will have to hide in a fagot
pile because he reads the New Testament and
believes that none but those who have repented
and believed should be baptized. Then every
man shall be at liberty to worship God as he
thinks right. Editha, I *know* that day of freedom
will come, and I am proud to think what part the
sacrifice of Anabaptist suffering and toil, yea, the
sacrifice of Anabaptist lives themselves, will have
in bringing freedom to the world!"

CHAPTER VIII

NEWS

I HAD climbed to the top of the fagot pile. It was so dark that mother thought no one would see me. I had been very careful not to make any more noise than I could help in climbing over the fagots. I was particularly careful also of some hard-boiled eggs. My own hen had laid the eggs, and I had boiled them. Mother always took the tenth egg for the priests; but she had taken all such eggs from her own store that I might have every single one for father. I was full of joy that I could carry him such a present.

I was holding my breath, and I had climbed as softly as might be to the very top of the fagot pile, when I heard a noise behind me, and looking toward the house, my eyes, grown accustomed to the darkness, faintly discerned two men stealthily coming around the corner. I crouched silently on the fagots, for I was very much frightened.

"They are after father!" was my thought.

By-and-by the two men disappeared around the house, and I, crouching there, afraid to stir, heard them knock on our door. I moved a little farther.

"Father!" I whispered, putting my face down to the hole.

For an answer I felt a hand reach out near me, and I gave him my basket. He set it down inside, and then almost noiselessly moved some fagots and lifted me into his place of hiding.

"Oh, father!" I whispered. "Two men are after you!"

I told him what I had heard and seen. He tried to calm me, saying that the men were not seeking him. And then I told him about the hard-boiled eggs, and he thanked me and said that I was a good, good girl to remember him, and he wanted me to stroke my hen for him the next day. He took one of the hard-boiled eggs and ate it, more to please and reassure me, I suppose, than to satisfy his own hunger.

We listened all the time, but heard nothing from the house, and at last father began to whisper to me without listening much more for outside sounds. He whispered, as was his wont, about the things he had read in the New Testament. And he had me feel with my hand, since I could not see, a place he had fixed among the fagots where he might hide the New Testament.

"I have been thinking much," he told me, "that it would not be right if I should have to go away somewhere else to hide, that I should carry the New Testament with me. For if I should be taken, Editha, and if I could never come back here again, the men who captured me would take the New Testament too, and then the last way in which you might ever be able to see

God's word might be gone. You might never be where you could get another Testament, Editha, and I cannot have my child grow up without knowing the way to heaven. So, Editha, if some-time you do not find me among these fagots, you may know that the New Testament is here, hid-den in this little spot. Read the book, Editha. It is God's word for his people, and no king has a right to say that common folk shall not be free to read it. The Lord sent it to the common folk, and woe to the priests who keep it from them.

"And I think," continued my father, "that the answer that John Wycliffe once gave is a good an-swer in these days. He said, 'The clergy cry aloud that it is heresy to speak of the Holy Scriptures in English, and so they would condemn the Holy Ghost who gave it in tongues to the apostles of Christ, to speak the word of God in all languages under heaven.'"

I stayed with my father longer than usual, for he hardly dared let me go back to the house, lest those two men should see me. And before he lifted me out of the hole he whispered a prayer to the Lord Jesus that I might be safe. My father told me to pray too, and I did pray that nobody might see me, or might think that father was hidden in the fagot pile. Then father and I kissed each other and father lifted me out, and I crept down the fagot pile very softly, on the side away from the house, and then I went on tip-toe toward our door, and at last dared go in.

Mother said the men had been after father. She looked very pale, and I knew she had been crying, but I told her that father said the Lord Jesus would keep us safe from harm. No one disturbed our household all night long after that; but I think my mother did not sleep much.

So the remaining months of that year wore away, my father hiding among the fagots. Sometimes, on the coldest nights, he came into the house. Several times men came to search, but they never came when he was elsewhere than in the great fagot pile, and no one seemed to suspect its secret; but my father felt that any day his retreat might be discovered, and he thought it best that he should try to find a hiding-place at a distance from our town.

"There must be coverts in the fields where a man might hide from the priests," judged my father. "If I cannot bide in such places, I will come back to the fagot pile."

So one night he fled, and my mother grieved till she was well-nigh heart-broken.

It was while my father was gone that the Lord 1530 High Chancellor Sir Thomas More, with A.D. the great ecclesiastics, issued a declaration against all English translations of the Scriptures. The first day I heard of that, I rashly climbed the fagot pile in the daytime, and boldly dropped myself down into the big hole where my father had not been hidden for a fortnight. I felt around in the fagots till I found the New Testament where my father said he would leave it. The great High Chancellor did not know that he had sent a child into a fagot heap to read the New Testament.

So there I sat for a long time poring over the book, and reading to myself such portions as I knew best. I found the place where was the prayer I read to old Neighbor Eld, the day before he died : " Oure Father which arte in heven, halowed be thy name. Let thy kingdom come. Thy wyll be fulfilled, as well in erth, as hit ys in heven. Geve vs this daye oure dayly breade. And forgeve vs oure treaspases, even as we forgeve them which treaspas vs. Leede vs not into temptacion, but delyvre vs from yvell. Amen."

I stayed in the fagot pile longer than I intended, but the reason was I did not find it so easy to climb out as I had anticipated. The hole was somewhat deep, and my footing a little insecure in making my exit. But I succeeded at last, and came hastily down from the fagot pile, much defiance of Sir Thomas More within my soul. I had done just what Sir Thomas said I should not do. I was triumphant! There was no right spirit of Bible reading within me. I wanted to read only because my father's enemy had said I should not. I did not know that over in Hamburg, across the sea, this same year William Tyndale was printing his translation of the five books of Moses. I had no knowledge, as I went back to the house from the fagot pile, that any additional part of the Bible was to be made ready for English folk.

"Where have you been, Editha?" asked my mother, when I came in. "Stephen wanted to find you, but I could not tell him where you were."

"I was in the fagot pile reading the New Testament," I whispered in her ear.

My mother started.

"Did father leave the book there?" she questioned softly.

"Yes," I answered. "He showed me where he would hide it. He wanted me to read it."

"Editha," and my mother spoke slowly, after a little pause, "the next time you go to the fagot pile, you may bring me the New Testament, if father is not there. I will read it a little, perhaps."

And often, after I brought her the book, I used to come across my mother secretly reading the New Testament. Mother carried the book around with her, and at night we hid it in our bed, and she and I talked in whispers about the strange things in the New Testament. After a while my mother showed the New Testament to my aunt, but instead of reading it at all, my aunt was so indignant at such a book being in our house that, if it had not been for the love she bore my mother, I believe the priests would have heard of this defiance of their authority.

From about this time, my mother ceased telling me saints' tales. Not that she had ceased to believe in the saints, but I think she had read enough of the New Testament to see that much of what she had thought true did not agree with that book, and she would think before talking much more about her past teaching. But my aunt told Stephen and me many saints' tales, with a sort of indignant emphasis that I thought I understood. She was not going to be deceived by the New Testament. But she was very prudent, and never once mentioned the book before me. Of course, Stephen knew nothing of it, and nothing of all my thinking and wondering about the Anabaptists.

One day, when father had been gone a good while and when mother was growing thin and worn day by day as she spun her wool, there came an unusual number of pilgrims to the shrine of our town, and Stephen and I went out to watch them. Among the villagers who looked on was one woman, ever spiteful with her tongue, and she came near me, and smiled and whispered: "Editha, when you go home, tell your mother that one of the pilgrims says she saw your father taken by the officers."

I gazed at her with widely open, terrified eyes, and then leaving Stephen I ran home, stifling my sobs as much as possible. A kind-hearted neighbor asked me what ailed me, and a boy said that a pilgrim had struck me, but I did not pause to give any answer. I ran on till I found my mother in the house, and sobbed out the news to her.

"Who told you?" she said, white and stern.

And when I spoke the woman's name, my mother declared : " I will not believe it ! I do not believe that any pilgrim told her such a thing ! It is her own spite."

Late that night my mother left the house, and went to the fagot pile. She had never failed to look there since my father went away, for she hoped for his return at any time. Little did I expect the news she brought back this night, however. I had thought she was a long time away, and I, worn out with the fright and crying of the day, was very nearly asleep when she came softly in, and creeping beside me, kissed me and whispered : " Editha, father is among the fagots again. Father has come back."

"Oh !" I cried.

Half asleep, I sat up, and my mother whispered to me the story, how father had been taken by some officers, but as they went on with him they came to a drinking-place, and going in they began to drink. When they had drunk a good deal, they fell asleep, and father, slipping out, hid from them. They waked and tried to find him, but he had hidden in a holly bush and was not discovered, and now he had come safely home again, and would stay awhile in the pile of fagots. Mother had given him some supper, and had carried him the New Testament, and father had sent me a kiss, and he would be very glad to rest and read a little, for he was very worn with travel and lack of food.

Oh, how long the next day seemed till night
came, and I could climb the fagot pile and see
father again! And how glad he was to see me!

So began again our watching over the fagot
pile that no one might find father's retreat. My
father brought us much news of how matters
stood in England. He said that there were men
who were being forced to abjure, and he had
heard of a man, John Ryburne, of a place in the
diocese of Lincoln, who had been accused by his
own sister of saying that the church service was
corrupt. Others of the same place were compelled to abjure, and a man named Thomas Hitton,
was burned in Kent, and John Tyndale was in
trouble for sending money to his brother beyond
sea, and a man named John Tyler, for opposing purgatory, and another named Thomas Cur-
son, for disregarding monkery and for having an
English Testament; and a man named Thomas
Cornwall was condemned to always be in prison,
because he tore off his badge after he had borne a
fagot. But Thomas Cornwall escaped. And one,
Thomas Philip, was in trouble too, for he had
Tracy's Testament, and ate butter in Lent.

My father told us also that there was a preacher
named Latimer, who had been a believer in Romish superstition, but had been converted, and had
become eager for the conversion of others. He
had begun preaching at Cambridge, where he was
also a private instructor in the university, and his
sermons had been so pointed against the foolish-

ness of praying in the Latin tongue and keeping the people in ignorance, that several of the resident friars and heads of houses had spoken against him. But he had silenced them by his severe criticisms and eloquent arguments the last Christmastide.

And John Skelton, the poet who had written such rhymes about the friars and the bishops was dead, my father brought word. He would never again write rhymes mocking the friars.

So my father had much news to tell, and none of it, as far as we saw, was very encouraging to those people who cared for the New Testament, except that it was a good thing the preacher Latimer had been converted.

My father had once told me of an archbishop of Mainz, who lived many, many years ago, and who, finding a Bible, and looking into it, said: "Of a truth I do not know what book this is, but I perceive everything in it is against us."

I wondered if some of the friars now, who thought the New Testament so dreadful a book for common people, ever read it, or whether the friars had read it and knew it was against them, and so were not willing that the English people should read it for themselves in their own tongue?

We rejoiced greatly that father was where we could see him again, and know where he was. I was so full of joy that I could hardly keep from telling Stephen. But that would never do.

We expected that the officers who had lost

father after capturing him might come and search our house. But, for some reason, perhaps because they did not know in what part of the country his home was, perhaps because they did not even know his name, they did not appear. And, after a while, father would come into the house sometimes secretly, to help mother by carding the wool that she spun. And sometimes father would hear me read some verses from the New Testament as he worked. And then he would go back and hide in the fagot pile again.

One day, I remember father told me that there had been an edict published over across the sea in Zurich, that any who should baptize by immersion should be put to death. Some Anabaptists had been taken under this law, and tied back to back and thrown into the water ; some had been burnt alive, and many starved in prison.

I was greatly impressed by this news, but afterward finding that Zurich was a very long way from England, I did not so much care for the edict, since my father assured me it had no force in our own country.

But my father told me that the Roman Catholics everywhere had always hated and persecuted the Anabaptists, and that I must never expect a priest to have any other feeling than a particular hatred toward us.

" It is not to be wondered at that Zurich drowns Anabaptists, since the reformer Zwingli, there, has been so taught by the Catholic church," remarked my father. "He does not clearly see in all things yet. I trust God leads him. Although indeed, Editha, hundreds of years ago, the Catholics did not themselves baptize infants, but baptized those persons who were old enough to understand about religious things, and to know the reason for baptism. But you need not tell the priests that nowadays, for it would only make them angry."

"Does everything that is right make them angry, father?" I asked.

My father sighed.

"I hope that God will enlighten even the Roman church, my child," he answered. "That church was once better than it is now. But I fear the eyes of the priests are willfully closed. The priests declare the Anabaptists accursed, because we reject infant baptism, and are 're-baptized,' as the priests say. They have said that for hundreds of years, but it is not true. We baptize but once. It is their baptism of infants that we reject, and the priests know it."

And I think it was after this talk with my father that, though ignorant of many of the proofs of the correctness of the Anabaptist belief as drawn from the teaching of the New Testament, I felt that I belonged with this persecuted people, and that I sympathized most heartily with the Anabaptists in their struggle for religious freedom. I did not realize how much more I was to know of that struggle within a few years

CHAPTER IX

FLIGHT

IT was dark. I half woke. My mother was sitting up in bed, and I sleepily wondered why.

I nearly slept again.

Suddenly there was a great crash, as of falling wood. Then a sound of quickly running feet, and of voices calling, and of a great deal of wood thrown hither and thither.

My mother sprang up with a half-suppressed cry, and ran away from me into the dark.

I sat up, my heart beating with fright.

"Mother!" I called.

I was so frightened that I could hardly speak. What was going on outdoors?

"Mother! mother!" I repeated.

I jumped to my feet, and ran to the outer door of the house. It was open. I caught hold of it, and trembling, peered outdoors. There was a very faint star-light. I could hear indistinct noises. Somebody ran swiftly by the door in the darkness. I heard some one else plunge in another direction. It seemed as if the big fagot pile had been thrown down. I could not see its top against the sky.

There were no more sounds.

I waited, and shivered, and cried silently.

"Oh, father, father!" I sobbed quietly to myself.

Something dreadful must have happened. I
stepped silently outside. Trembling, I walked
noiselessly toward the fagot heap till I found myself stumbling over fagots. They were scattered
far and wide.

I dared not make a sound. I went back to the
house, and stood at the door. Where had my
mother gone? Had the men killed my father?
Was my mother dead too? I did not dare to shut
the door, for it seemed to me that somebody might
have entered the house while I had walked toward
the fagot heap. I looked at the dark, back of me
in the room, and fancied I heard some one move
in the blackness.

By-and-by two figures came toward me from
the outer darkness. I shrank back as the two entered the room.

"Editha," whispered a voice.

It was my mother. She fastened the door, hurried me silently into my day clothing, forbade my
speaking, and then moved about, evidently putting
some things into a bag. I could feel some one else
moving about the room. I knew it was my aunt,
but the two women did not say anything.

After a while my aunt kissed me, and then my
mother took my hand and led me outdoors.

My aunt shut the door behind us, and mother

and I set off in the dark, she carrying the bag and holding my hand. I did not dare to talk. I could only wonder, as we went softly on, where we were going. Once we passed over what seemed to be a very shallow stream. My mother lifted me across, and then we went on as before, only I helped her carry the bag. And so we walked a long time till we hid near some bushes, and mother gave me something to eat out of the bag. It was nearly morning.

"Are we going to walk all day, mother," I whispered.

"No," she answered. "We will not walk any more till night."

And when night came again we did walk a long way till we came to a thicket and a wall, where we hid in the dark. All about us in the field was a multitude of white spots, that as sunrise drew near, turned into sheep. There were so many sheep, more than I had ever seen before. But I was so sleepy and tired that, as I lay with my head in my mother's lap, I saw the sheep less and less, and by-and-by not at all, for I slept soundly.

When I awoke, mother was sitting yet, with widely open, tired, watchful eyes ; and one of the sheep was eating grass not far from us. I watched the creature's movements with great delight till I was more awake, and then I remembered about father.

"Where is father, mother?" I asked.

She looked at me.

"Do not talk, Editha," she whispered. "Some one might be on the other side of the wall, and might hear us."

So hushed I tried to keep quiet through the morning, though indeed it seemed a long time to have to stay in a thicket and not talk. If it had not been for the many sheep I do not know how I could have passed the time. There was one lamb that came near the thicket, and I tried to have the creature allow me to pat it, but the lamb was as wild as its mother, and would by no means trust to my friendship.

And as I looked at my mother, and found her always sitting, white-faced and anxious-eyed, I felt more and more worried about father. Why did he not come? I lost interest in the sheep, and at last I sat listening as my mother had set me the example of doing. It was afternoon when I dared again ask mother my early morning question.

"Mother," I whispered, noting the drawn look of her face and the fear of her manner, "where is father?"

"Perhaps we shall know before long," she answered, under her breath.

We stayed there all day.

Toward evening my mother broke forth in agony.

"Oh, Editha, Editha!" she begged. "Pray for father. He said he would come here if he were alive. I prayed to the saints for him all night. And we came here and did not find him. I was so in hopes he would be here before we came, and now all day has gone by, and he is not here. Oh, Editha, do you know how to pray to the Lord Christ himself? Did father teach you how? I am afraid father would not like to have me pray to the saints for him, but I could not help it. Can you pray to the Lord Christ, Editha?"

My poor mother! She was sobbing. She sobbed so that I could hardly put my childish petition into words, as I knelt beside her in the thicket. But she heard some of the words that I said, and she sobbed them over and over again, praying the Lord to send my father safely to us. And this, I think, was the first time my mother ever prayed, save to the Virgin and the saints.

That night my mother gave me something more to eat out of the bag, and got some water from a brook, and then once more the darkness came, and the sheep turned to white spots in the field, and I was sleepy, and I prayed the Lord's Prayer in English, and went to sleep. I half woke once in the night, and I heard my mother whisper: "Lord Christ, if thou wilt send my husband back to me, I will pray to thee, and not to the saints, all the rest of my life."

Then I slept more soundly, and heard nothing till I woke once more and found my mother sitting yet with widely open, tired, watchful eyes, and the white spots in the field had all turned to sheep again, for the sun was rising. Mother gave me some bread, and we stayed still among the

bushes.   Once in a while we heard a sound, and
mother seemed to hold her breath to listen.   Then,
perhaps the sheep that had made the sound
would come in sight, and mother would lean back
farther among the bushes.

But toward evening we heard a noise the other
side of the wall.   Mother turned very pale.   She
motioned me to be still.

But a man jumped over the wall, and as I saw
his face, I sprang up and ran, forgetting all caution
in my joy.

"Oh, father, father!" I cried.

He ran toward me and caught me in his arms.
A moment more, and we were all three hidden
among the bushes, my mother sobbing, and my
father's arms around us both.   It seemed as though
my mother could never stop crying.   To think
that father had escaped the men, after all!

"I had been almost asleep in the hole among
the fagots," my father told us, "when I thought
I heard a noise of some one coming softly up the
pile.   I thought perhaps it was one of you, though
why you came I could not tell.   I felt that some
one climbed to the top of the pile, and moved some
fagots, and I thought I saw a man's head between
me and the sky.   I felt an arm reach down and
grasp me, and I sprang up and grappled with the
man, and we struggled hither and yon, and
knocked down a great many fagots; and another
man came, and I ran, and they after, but in the
dark I escaped, and I have come a long, rounda-

bout road hither. The worst thing was, I feared
I should not find you here, I was so long coming,
and I dreaded lest ill should befall you, or lest you
should not dare to wait here."

And my mother, who had wept through all his
words, sobbed still as she answered : " Oh, Ralph,
Ralph ! We prayed to the Lord Christ for you !
Oh, Ralph, I feared you were dead ! "

My father wept somewhat himself. Then he
looked in our bag, and we all ate something, and
my father repeated some words from the New
Testament, because it was too dark to see to read
in the book. I was so glad he had saved the New
Testament, and not been obliged to leave it behind.

My father prayed in English, and so did my
mother and I, and again the sheep turned to white
spots in the field, and again I slept. But I think
that this time my mother slept too, for she knew
that though homeless, we were all together. Her
greatest anxiety was gone.

As I was going to sleep, or when I was awake a
moment in the night, I had a fleeting remembrance of the story that father had told us about
those Publicans who years ago were thrust out
into English fields to die of cold and hunger.
And I remembered that he had said that such
people were not called Publicans now, but were
called Anabaptists, and that Neighbor Eld had
been an Anabaptist, and that he himself was
one. Supposing we had to die in the fields like
those Publicans !

"I do not care," I thought sleepily, as I reached out my hand and felt father's hand lying near me. "I am going to be an Anabaptist too, just like father."

Then without realizing what such a resolution meant, I went to sleep again.

From what my father and mother whispered to each other very early the next morning, when I was half awake on my father's shoulder, I learned that my aunt would doubtless be much relieved to have such dangerous persons as my father and my mother safely away from the village. Sorry as my aunt might be for us, we were a constant menace to her hold on the favor of the priests and to her consequent security. She might go on pilgrimages, and might give tithes, but if she continually came to see and be friendly with a family suspected of heresy, how should she be safe? With us away, she could make her peace with the priests. She, perhaps, might be able to save a little of what we left behind us, and, if a time of religious freedom ever came to England, perhaps we might go back home. But that would not be yet.

And then I awoke more fully to realize what was meant.

"Shall I never see Stephen any more?" I asked, ready to cry at the loss of my daily companion, the one with whom I had been brought up, and whom I loved as I might have loved a brother. "Shall I never see Stephen again?"

My father soothed me quietly.

"I hope you will, Editha," he replied; "but not now."

Before it was quite light my father left us, for he was going to try and find a man he knew, one who bore on his cheek the branded mark accorded to him once as a gospeller. The man often came this way, my father told us, and could guide us, or tell us the way to a certain farmhouse where the good man and his wife both read the New Testament and believed it so much that they would hide us from the priests for a day or two; and then, after that my father thought we must try to find our way to the seacoast and out of England.

It was almost night-time again before father came back to us. Mother had become quite worried lest he had fallen into evil hands after all. But he had not, only he had tried to be so cautious that the errand had taken him a long time. He knew the way to the farmhouse now, and after dusk we thankfully followed him through the fields till we came at last to the home we sought, where the goodman and his wife welcomed us most heartily.

"God's people are one family in evil times like these," said the goodman's wife.

"I crave shelter but for a few days," answered my father gratefully. "We are going over the sea."

The next evening a thing came to pass which

impressed me very much. The gospeller who had directed my father to our place of refuge, came himself there, and, when it was nearly dusk, went with us to a little stream a short distance from the farmhouse. There the gospeller baptized my father and my mother, for my mother had entreated that she might also be baptized.

"I believe in the Lord Jesus Christ, who has forgiven me my sins," she affirmed.

And truly I think that always after that agonized night of watching in the thicket beside the wall my mother was a changed woman. Never again did she seem to doubt or waver, and never afterward did she pray to the Virgin or to the saints. In the blackness of that night, her soul's eyes had been opened. The gospeller believed now that she was a Christian, and he granted her wish for baptism.

I stood with the goodman and his wife on the edge of the little stream and saw through the shadows the gospeller baptize my father and my mother. An awe came over my spirit. I took hold of the goodman's wife's hand and she pressed mine, and we were still.

The branded-cheeked gospeller came up out of the water with my father and my mother. I should never forget it, never.

I was the more impressed by it because my father, before I went to sleep that night explained to me that while baptism does not save one's soul, still the ordinance is of Christ's appointing, and

In Editha's Days   The Twilight Baptism   Page 108

each of his followers should go at his command down into a burial in the water and rise again to a new life. I understood it all very clearly, and I also understood my father's explanation, when he told me that I was yet really unbaptized, for that was no baptism which the priest had given me when I was a baby, since the New Testament tells us to believe and be baptized, and I could not have believed first, being an infant.

"Ah, my child, do you know what it is to believe in the Lord Jesus now that you are old enough to do so?" asked my father. "Not till you do that, Editha, not till you have peace with God through knowing that Jesus has forgiven you all your sins, will you be ready to be baptized. Do not trust that the water of your infant baptism can save your soul, Editha. Had I known what I know now, I would not have allowed the priest to put you in the water fourteen years ago."

CHAPTER X

SAFETY AND SEPARATION

IT was two days afterward. My mother put up her hand in silent warning.

Rap! rap! rap! came a tapping at the door.

My mother and I hid. The goodman's wife kept silence.

Rap! rap! went on the sound persistently, again and again. Some one was stepping softly outside the door. We were all still.

"Oh, let me in! Let me in!" softly begged a woman's voice in distressed tones. "Oh, as you love your lives, let me in!"

My mother started at the first word, and looked at the goodman's wife.

"Let me in!" entreated the woman's voice at the door, as though she knew, notwithstanding our silence, that we were there within. "Let me in! Let me in!"

A lad's voice was added to the woman's.

"Let us in, Editha," he begged. And my mother sprang up, and ran to the door, and flung it open, and cast her arms about the woman there, and clung to her and the boy, and drew them into the room, shutting the door quickly after them.

Stephen ran straight to me.

"You must go away from here," gasped my aunt. "Oh, I thought perhaps the priests had found you. I have been seeking you two days. Oh, if they had found you, I would have been a murderer. I told them where you had gone. I could not help it. It was at the confession. The priest made me tell. I did not know where you would go, after you waited under the wall you told me you were bound for. But I had to tell the priest about the wall, and about your going in the night. Oh, sister, forgive me; I had to tell."

My aunt had flung herself on her knees beside my mother, and was panting out words with hurried sobbing.

"Oh, where is Ralph?" questioned my aunt. "The priests may find you any moment. I thought I should never find you. I should not, but I found a gospeller. I knew he was one by the branded cheek, and I threw myself on my knees to him, and begged him to tell me if he had seen you. Oh, go! go! The priests are hunting for you. Where is Ralph?"

The goodman's wife went outdoors to find her husband and my father. They were outdoors by day, my father keeping hidden, yet both watching lest some of the priests' messengers should come stealthily on the house.

After coming in and talking a little, my father decided that in a few hours, when it grew dark,

we would go.   The goodman's wife hid us all
carefully.   Her husband went outdoors to look at
the sheep and to watch for priests' messengers,
and his wife began to cook what she had, that we
might have supper before going and that we
might have some food to take with us.

The older ones who lay hidden whispered a
little, but Stephen and I were bidden not to
speak.

My aunt yet condemned herself that she had
been obliged to tell the priest of the direction in
which we went.

"Oh, I could not help it; I could not," she
sobbed, addressing my father.   "I went to confession, and the priest would know whether I had
known all these months that you were in the fagot
heap.   And I had to tell him that I did know ;
and he asked how I had dared come to confession
all these months and not tell him of that.   He
was so angry I thought he would kill me or curse
my soul.   He made me tell which way you went.
And I started that night, and walked and hunted
day and night since, for I thought—I thought—"

My aunt's voice broke.

"They cannot find us unless God wills it so,"
answered my father calmly.   "Peace, woman,
peace."

My aunt wept on.

"We will guide you back to your way first," my
father promised her, "then we will go ours."

"Your way is mine !" almost fiercely returned

my aunt. "I have suffered enough. I could have struck myself for a coward that night when I let my only sister and her child go away alone in the dark. I have always been near my sister, and I will be with her wherever you and your New Testament and your Anabaptist folly take her. I will not go back."

"The priests will take your possessions and ours," my father would have reminded her, but my mother cast her arms about my aunt, and the two women wept together.

And so, Romanists and Anabaptist "heretics" together, we five went away through the sheep fields that evening, taking with us that which we had saved as most necessary. And a strange difference there was in our thinking, for my father, besides all our food and what wrappings we had, carried with him the New Testament. And my aunt, besides her other treasures, had her rosary and a little bottle of the holy water she had got on her pilgrimage to Reading, and in her purse she carried a cross of palm made by the priest on last Palm Sunday, it having, she believed, the power to keep the evil one away from her. I suppose she thought she was likely to meet him, going off as she was with Anabaptists. Moreover, among her things my aunt carried her holy candles, hallowed by prayer and the sprinkling of holy water by the priest and afterward given her by him. Any Romish person could light such a candle in time of thunderstorms and feel safe.

H

Holy candles were also to be lighted when a person lay dying. And I know not how much more such rubbish my aunt carried with her; for though she left home for my mother's sake, yet she by no means gave up her religion, and perhaps she thought that the cross of palm and the holy candles might even keep harm from such heretics as we were. And I myself heard my aunt mutter a prayer to St. Leonard to keep us from prison.

But my aunt did not particularly desire to call my father's attention to what she carried, and I think she was afraid I might speak, for before starting she greatly bewailed to me that she could not have brought with her an earthen pot that for years she had used in cooking.

"What shall I do when I want to cook in the Low Countries you say we are going to?" she inquired of me.

But she asked no such questions of my elders, and I think she spoke so to me merely because she thought that was a question that might turn away my observation from the mass of useless things she did bring.

But, poor soul, she could hadly be expected to drop all her superstitions at once. I did not say a word about what she had brought, and I think no one but myself saw the contents of her bundle before we started.

So we walked softly through the fields, stumbling again and again over some sheep, for there were very many of the creatures. My father thought if we could but follow the river Kennet down to where it joins the Thames, and from thence go eastward to the coast of the sea in Essex or Kent, or perhaps stop at London and take voyage from there, we might do best. We had but a little store of money among us, yet we trusted there might be enough to take us away from King Henry's realm and help us begin life in a new country.

" We shall reach a better land than England," defiantly declared my aunt, stalking on. " This is not a land for honest folk."

She seemed to have taken charge of all of us; and indeed she was always a self-reliant woman, though perhaps rendered more so by the number of years she had been a widow, her husband having died shortly after Stephen's birth.

We had gone on but a little while. The night was deepening about us. I looked back and discerned the dark form of my aunt. She was standing still. Soon she came hastening on behind us with long, silent strides. She caught my mother by the arm.

" There are men ! " whispered my aunt. " I heard one call to another. They are coming behind us. And one is a monk of Caversham. I know his voice."

There was no copse in which we might hide. The only thing we could do, in all the broad expanse of those fields, was to drop down among the sheep, trusting that the number of them and the darkness, might hide us, if it were God's will. We could not tell in just which direction our foes might come. That they were our foes we did not doubt, since the monk of Caversham was among them.

The sheep were too sleepy to mind our presence and betray us by commotion. I dropped down between two of the white creatures. In a few minutes we heard the footsteps of the men who walked the fields, talking cautiously to one another. I too recognized the voice of that monk of Caversham. Evidently the men had not seen us, for they talked of their purpose of finding the man at whose house they supposed us to be yet hiding. Fierce threats were made of what should be done with us, threats of branding, of whipping, of starvation, of burning. I nestled closer to the sleeping sheep, and a great quaking shook me with fear.

The monk's voice was very near. He stumbled over a sheep, and his outstretched hand almost touched my shoulder, as he cried out with rage at his fall.

"The heretics shall pay for this," he muttered, smiting the unfortunate sheep. "I would every heretic in England were burned, but I would I had the burning of them. I would not burn them whole. Not I. May our Lady and St. Dominic send me the day when I can burn an Anabaptist piecemeal!"

He had risen and walked a few steps and now he stumbled over another sheep.

"Come!" chided another voice, angrily; "you have drunk so much you cannot walk. If you found an Anabaptist to-night, he could outrun you."

They passed on, and their voices died away. We hid among the sheep for an hour or more. Then we went forward, and journeyed all that night, my aunt continually muttering prayers to the saints for our safety. I doubt not she thought that her cross of palm had delivered us from the monk.

This was the nearest approach to capture in all our nights of travel before we reached the coast of Essex. There we hid and endured much hardship and peril, till we thought that all our journey had been in vain, so did we despair of being able to evade the officers and find shipment for the Low Countries. But at last we heard of a vessel that would wait at a certain point for us, and through the kindness of some fisher-folk we were conducted one night across the flat Essex marshes and taken in a small boat to the vessel.

Oh, it was blessed to be fully away from England! And it was blessed at last to draw near land again, to reach the Low Countries, and to feel ourselves out of King Henry's realm. We would forget past hardships, and try to make a new home. So came we to our next place of refuge.

We were not so very far from a village, Scheveningen, about two miles from the Hague, or

s'Gravenhage, as the Dutch call that city. The
village Scheveningen is on the downs that spread
to the North Sea. The downs are composed of
ranges of hillocks of sand. Gray skies, misty
horizons, the glimpse of numerous fishermen who
lived in the village out of sight across the downs,
flocks of curlews and gulls sweeping at times
ovehead; thin, scattered grass, a little broom and
rosemary, waves that rushed with a prolonged
lament against the shore, these are among the
first sights I had in the Low Countries. Sometimes we went on land, and walked a good way
toward the village, and saw drawn upon the
beach the vessels of the herring fishery, each
boat with its one mast and great, square sail.

But we ourselves lived out of reach or sight
of the sea, on a canal that led to the Hague.
We lived in a *treckschuyt*, for we had been so
blessed as to obtain one of those large boats, an
old one, no longer used, as the *treckschuyten* com-
monly are, in carrying passengers from one place
to another. Our *treckschuyt* was made so that it
was almost filled with a kind of a house, divided
into two parts. At the prow was an iron bar with
a ring, meant for the passing through it of a long
rope, to be fastened at one end near the helm, and
at the other end attached to a horse on the canal
bank. But we had no horse, and did not intend
to journey. My father had managed to obtain
this shelter for us only because the *treckschuyt*
was very old, and the man who had formerly used

it had, after saving diligently, been able to buy another one.

It delighted me to find that instead of living in a house, we were going to have our home in this large boat. So many people lived in boats, and my father said it might be more safe for us to do so. Stephen rejoiced, and we learned as fast as possible to talk the queer language we heard, in order to be able to speak to the neighbors in the other boats.

And I was so glad that I had learned to read. I should have felt disgraced if I had not known how to read English, since of course I could not read Dutch, and all the people, even the poorest of the boatmen, were so much better educated than the common folk of England. And if I, at fourteen, had not been able to read, how shocking it would have seemed! I did not tell people, though, that the New Testament had been the book in which I learned to read. For father thought that even in this land perhaps we would do best to be careful what we said to other people. And we found that it was indeed so. But we talked all we pleased to each other on those days when my father, who had a little boat, took us with him fishing. There were many fish in the Scheveningen district, and I do not remember any happier days than those we spent fishing. We felt so safe and happy. Father told us that in 1416 the first great herring net was made. It was made at Hoorn, the ancient capital of North

Holland, and my father told Stephen and me about the fishing for herring and cod. It was not like the old days when I had had to climb stealthily up the fagot pile to whisper to my father.

Many a time I looked out on the waters now, and sang, and prophesied to myself: "We shall never have any more trouble. Our boat is like Noah's ark, that my father has told me about. We are safe in this boat from all trouble."

Oh, calm, sweet days, spent on the water, free from all harm, you were the last, the last dear days of home life together! I did not prize those days then as I would have prized them, if I had known. What to us were the plots of King Henry of England, his stake, the hatred of the priests, and the curse of the pope? We fished and sang.

The people around us were honest and industrious and trustworthy. Everybody worked. It seemed good to love and trust everybody, and to sing and work in our boat-home. My aunt had to listen to the reading of the New Testament. But she did not oppose it so strongly as she would once have done, and Stephen, convinced of his ignorance in the matter of reading, zealously set himself to learn his letters, that he might not be despised by the people.

And after I could well understand the language, I heard an Anabaptist woman tell my mother the story of Felix Mantz, who had been a great leader among the Reformers, and who had preached about baptism, wishing that people should be believers before they were baptized. He preached in various parts of Switzerland, and in the fields and the woods he explained the word of God to the people who came to hear him. The magistrates of Zurich did not like this, and thought Mantz a rebel. So toward the end of 1526, he was put in prison in the tower of Wellenberg.

Mantz confessed that he had baptized, contrary to the edict, and said that it is right to obey God rather than man. And so he was condemned to be drowned.

"He was taken from the tower of Wellenberg to the fish market," said the woman, "and as he went he praised God for allowing him to die for the truth. For he said that anabaptism is right, and founded on the word of God. Mantz's mother and brother came to him on the way, and told him to be firm. And he was. For God gave Felix Mantz such grace that when he was bound on the hurdle, and the executioner was about to throw him into the water, Mantz sung with a loud voice, 'Into thy hands, O Lord, I commend my spirit.' And then the executioner drowned him."

My mother sighed.

"Do you know," continued our new friend, "I cannot think how a person can be a real Christian, and yet drown another person. Felix Mantz left a writing behind him that said, 'It is set before him who will be an heir with Christ, that he must be merciful, even as his Heavenly Father is merciful. Christ never accused any one, as the false teachers now do ; whence it appears that they have not the love of Christ, nor understand his word.'"

But though we heard such tales, yet something persuaded us that trouble would not come to us in this boat-home. It seemed as though one might sail away, and never have anything more to do with priest or king, but forget that any such persons ever tried to bind one's soul or take one's life. I think that our manner of living so filled my father with the joy of freedom that he was at first somewhat blind to the real state of things in the country.

Moreover, my father told Stephen and me what he had heard happened last year in Switzerland, to the images in the churches at Wesen. Some deputies there had threatened the people, but the young men courageously took the images out of the churches, carried the images to an open place near a lake, and cried out to them, as if they had really been living saints, who could hear and understand : "Look ! this road (that by the lake) leads to Coire and to Rome ; that (to the south) to Glaris ; this other (to the west) to Schwytz ; and the fourth (by the Ammon) to St. Gall. Take which you please. But if you do not move off, you shall be burnt."

The young men then waited a few minutes, to give the images a seemingly fair chance perhaps, and then threw them into the fire. There was quite a stir over this affair.

I used to wonder if the image of Our Lady in the little town of Caversham, whence we came, would ever be thrown into the fire that way. I hardly wanted the angel of the spear-head to be treated so, though I now knew him to be an impostor. But he had been the friend and wonder of Stephen and myself, and while I knew the angel was a cheat, yet I had a strange sort of affection for him. Perhaps I may as well say here, lest I should forget it, as I go on telling my story, that in an after year, that one-winged angel of the spear-head did come to grief. For when the other impostures of the monasteries were being discovered in England, about eight years after our flight from that country, the one-winged angel was condemned, and was sent to London to be exhibited there. No one need ever believe in the angel of the spear-head any more. He was further disgraced by having had sent away with him "a piece of the halter with which Judas hanged himself."

As the days of our sojourn in the Low Countries went by, and winter came, the canal froze, and the skating began, and the sleds and sledges went whizzing by our *treckschuyt*, and sometimes even the boats of the fishing-village of Scheveningen went flying past on the ice, with sails all set. We would see peasants skating like arrows. Stephen and I could not think of attaining such speed and skill. We thought this a pleasant home to which we had come to live. So we sang and worked and were very happy. And yet our peaceful days were soon shadowed. Indeed, I do not think my father well knew to what a realm we had fled. He only knew that England was not large, and that on the continent some men found safety from the priests and from King Henry's decrees. But I know, for my father told me, that before coming to the Netherlands he had never heard of the decree issued by the Emperor Charles against the followers of Martin Luther. This edict, issued in 1521, said: "As it appears that the aforesaid Martin is not a man, but a devil under the form of a man, and clothed in the dress of a priest, the better to bring the human race to hell and damnation, therefore all his disciples and converts are to be punished with death and forfeiture of all their goods."

The provinces, unfortunately, were the private property of Charles V., and he could do as he pleased. So this bloody edict was of course carried out. The first of July, 1523, two Augustine monks were burned at Brussels for having believed in Lutheranism. These were the first, but they were not the last victims in the provinces.

Charles had another edict published in the Netherlands, forbidding all private assemblies for devotion; all reading of the Scriptures; all discussion within one's own house about faith, the sacraments, the authority of the pope, or other religious matters. Whoever did any of these things should die. And many did suffer at the stake.

And, though it is going beyond my story at present, I may as well say now that the number of Netherlanders who were burned, strangled, or buried alive, according to the decrees of the Emperor Charles, for the offense of reading the Scriptures, of looking askance at a graven image, or of ridiculing the idea that Christ is actually present in body and blood in the sacrament of the Supper, has been thought to be perhaps as high as one hundred thousand, and never has been estimated as less than fifty thousand.

Had my father realized how bigoted and cruel an emperor Charles V. was, I doubt whether we would have gone from England to the Low Countries. And yet I do not know where else we could have gone. My father grew more troubled month by month in our new home. He and my mother held long, secret talks, and I, grown sharper-witted by the perils we had undergone, knew that all was not right.

Finally, in February, 1531, a short time after our arrival, a command went abroad that no Anabaptist preacher should be harbored in the Netherlands. A reward was offered for the capture of any such. And, immediately after this, an edict was issued declaring that those persons who had been *re-baptized* (as it was called), should be punished with the utmost severity, if they continued obstinate. If they recanted, they should find mercy.

This edict revealed to us what our future was

to be. And there came to us, soon after the edict was made known, a piece of news from Friesland that made us more certain that danger was upon us to no small degree. Friesland, as you know, is one of the provinces of Holland, and is on the larger sea and the Zuyder-Zee, so being quite near us.

A man named Sicke Snijder, or Freerks, was baptized on confession of his faith after the edict was issued. He was taken prisoner, and, after suffering much, and not recanting, was sentenced by the court of Friesland as follows : " Sicke Freerks, on this 20th of March, 1531, is condemned by the court to be executed with the sword, his body shall be laid on the wheel, and his head set upon a stake, because he has been rebaptized, and perseveres in that baptism."

So, by the sword, went this Baptist out of this life into that which is eternal. It was not ministers alone who were to suffer. If a poor Anabaptist tailor must die for his belief, would not many more of us be condemned also ?

" To be executed by the sword, to have one's body laid on a wheel, and one's head set on a stake," I heard my mother say to my father, " it is horrible ! "

But my father answered her in the words of the New Testament, " ' It is enough for the disciple that he be as his master, and the servant as his lord.' ' And fear not them which kill the body, but are not able to kill the soul.' ' He that loseth his life for my sake shall find it.' "

Yet my father, with all his faith, did not know what important thing the death of the poor Anabaptist tailor was to accomplish. For it was through Snyder's death that that afterward distinguished Anabaptist, Menno Simon, was first led to more of the truth concerning baptism. For Menno Simon himself says: "It now happened that I heard from some brethren that a God-fearing, pious man, Sicke Snyder by name, had been beheaded at Leeuwarden, because he had renewed his baptism. This sounded wonderfully in my ears, that any one should speak of another baptism. I searched the Scriptures with diligence, and reflected earnestly upon them, but could find no trace of infant baptism."

To us it was very evident that, as he hated the Lutherans, so Charles V. hated the Anabaptists.

And still, living as we were among the boat-people, we had for a time no especial trouble. Many a poor fleeing Anabaptist preacher did we hide in our *treckschuyt* from the death that awaited him on land. And my father sometimes helped carry such preachers away in our smaller boat to better hiding places. And it was in our boat-home that Stephen and I both at last came to know the Lord Jesus Christ as our own Saviour, who forgave us our sins according to his promise, "Him that cometh to me I will in no wise cast out." Oh, if in those comparatively peaceful days I had not found the Lord, how should I have borne the distress that came soon?

One of the hiding Anabaptist preachers, for whose apprehension a reward had been offered, and whom we were concealing in our *treckschuyt*, baptized me one winter night, breaking the thin ice to do so. My aunt refused to let Stephen be baptized, and he was much grieved about it. But I think my aunt hoped to win him back to saint-worship and to Rome's power again, and planned the next spring to have a boat separate from us, and so keep him from my father's influence.

Most dreadful times came. There was talk of the Spanish Inquisition. There had been inquisitors in the Netherlands before. I do not know why my father did not flee from the Netherlands. I think he thought of doing so. We had been now two years there. I was sixteen. My aunt had accomplished her design, and was now living 1532 with Stephen in another boat, not a *treck-* A.D. *schuyt* like ours, but of good size.

One day, toward evening, some men came down upon us so suddenly that it confuses me now when I think of it. We—my father, my mother, and I—were hurried away as prisoners, charged with having harbored Anabaptist preachers, and with being Anabaptists ourselves. On shore my father and my mother were hastened in one direction, I was taken in another. I never saw them again. I do not know what became of them. I can guess, but the thought is too horrible.

When we were surprised by our captors the

English New Testament was hidden on board our boat. None of us had time to take the book, and I comforted myself afterward for its loss by thinking that perhaps Stephen and my aunt might come in their boat, and discover what had been done with us, and look in the usual hiding-place for the New Testament, and finding, read it. My aunt's boat had been out of sight at the time of our capture. It would be a great shock to my aunt to find out what had occurred. But I thought neither of the New Testament nor of my aunt at the moment of separation.

I caught one last glimpse of my mother's face as the men hastened her away. I would not say to myself that it was the last look. I yet had hope that we might in some way escape. I had supposed that as a matter of course we three would be kept together, would share one another's troubles, would perhaps be put to death together. I thought it would be sweet to enter heaven together.

But when, immediately after reaching the shore, the men had separated us, I cried out in alarm, and my mother succeeded in turning her head and giving me that last look. Ah, mother-face, never again, never again to be seen on earth! My father was already so hurried ahead that he could give me neither word nor look.

Ah, it will not matter, when I enter heaven, when I see waiting there the two dear home-faces, when I hear them cry, "My child," when I feel

I

my father's and my mother's arms around me once again, it will not matter then that we were so cruelly torn apart. There we can talk peacefully of the past.

But at the time of our sudden separation, I was overwhelmed, and I wept so bitterly that I did not notice at all which way I was taken. I knew it was to some building where I was put into a very small room, and then I threw myself down and for a long time sobbed out my heart-break.

In the midst of my weeping, however, the door opened again, and another girl was pushed into the cell. A little food was given us, but neither she nor I could eat.

Sitting in darkness that did not allow us to see one another's face, we both sobbed for a time. She told me that her name was Thyra, and that she also was the daughter of Anabaptists. I had never seen nor known of her in the past.

It was not till the night was perhaps half gone that sleep came to still my tears and calm my aching head. I suppose that it was morning when I woke, judging from the length of dim daylight that followed. I had slept heavily from grief and exhaustion. I could see that Thyra, who I thought was a girl two or three years younger than I, was awake. She did not look as if she had slept at all. She was sitting, gazing forward intently. There was something in her appearance that startled me a little at first, but I did not speak to her. I was thinking how much good Anabaptists had done in the Netherlands in the past ; how many they had drawn from the Romish church ; how many they had taught to believe in the true way of salvation.

" And now the Emperor Charles will kill every Anabaptist he can find," I thought. " No wonder so devout a Romanist as he, thinks that we are worthy of death."

I felt a great longing to know what had become of my father and my mother. Oh, should I never see them again ? I buried my face and sobbed till I could sob no more. And my poor roommate. Did she also grieve over her loved ones ?

I looked steadfastly at Thyra. But her gaze was far enough away.

Suddenly a great shudder shook her, and she turned wild eyes upon me.

" Is it once, or is it twice ? " she screamed. " Is it once, or is it twice ? Oh ! "

She covered her ears with her hands, and shuddered.

" Thyra ! Thyra ! What is it ? " I cried, striving to soothe her.

But she, still shuddering with what seemed to be horror, put me away. Her light hair fell from its fastening, and she caught at the locks and pressed them to her ears as if to shut out some awful sound. Then a seeming madness fell upon her, and she rushed at the walls, striking them as if she would push them over. Unheeding the bruised palms of her feeble hands, she struck unceasingly till I caught and held and tried to calm her. And then she broke out in wild weeping.

All that day she seemed in a kind of maze, and I, watching her, feared lest our imprisonment was beginning to affect her mind. Sometimes she slept, but ever and anon she would spring half-up and look at me with a face so horror-struck that I felt a chill go over me.

When night came, I was very hungry, and I was sure Thyra must be too, though some horror held her mind fast and would not let it go, wherefore it might be that she did not feel her hunger keenly. We had eaten the very small amount of food given us the night before.

I lay down and slept at last. But I woke in the depths of the night. Thyra was asleep. Through the prison walls I had heard some sounds that had waked me. They came again, dreadful, choking sounds, and then one voice after another cried, tauntingly, "Is it once, or is it twice? Is it once, or is it twice?"

I thought I dreamed at first. They were the same words that Thyra had screamed.

But I could not mistake. Through the wall came a faint sound as of some one trying to speak, and then men's voices cried again: "Is it once, or twice? Re-baptizer, is it once, or twice?"

Then there was a rush, as of men who set upon a prisoner and choked him. There were a few gasping sounds, dreadful, horrible, so that I shut my ears and lay shaking with terror.

"Re-baptizer." I had heard the word. I was sure I had. Now I knew what that question meant: "Is it once, or twice?"

"To baptize again." For that is what the name Anabaptist means, and the German word "*Wied-ertäufen*." It was an unjust name to give us, since of course we did not immerse any one twice, but only once, not recognizing the baptism of the church of Rome as the true baptism taught by our Lord Jesus Christ in the New Testament.

Oh, that horrible, horrible night. It seemed as though a number of men were torturing the prisoner by taking turns in choking him, allowing him time to recover between each onslaught. There came a series of dreadful, gasping, strangling sounds that I shuddered to hear, and yet listened to, being held by horror. The Anabaptist was gaining his breath.

"Let him have a little more breath, just a little more," sneered one voice, "and we will try it again."

"Now! Now! Another chance. Another!" cried one, with the enjoyment of a fiend in it. "Re-baptizer, is it once, or is it twice? Once or twice?"

A shriek pierced the walls. I sprang up, shaking so that I could hardly stand. How could Thyra sleep? The cold sweat stood on my face. I shut my ears and sprang from that side of the cell to the other. Oh, horror, horror! What awful deed was this? I crouched in the far corner of my cell,

my ears tightly shut, my head against the wall,
that last scream ringing through my brain, and I
prayed that deafness might fall upon me. For so
wrought was I that it seemed as if those heart-
chilling sounds pierced through the walls and
through my hard-pressing fingers into my very
brain in spite of my effort.

It appeared to me that hours went by; but it
was thick blackness yet when at last I ventured
to remove my hands from my ears and listen. I
heard nothing. Numb from my long kneeling,
trembling with cold, I crept back beside Thyra,
and lay down. My widely open eyes stared at
the dark. What form of ghastliness might lie on
the other side the wall? Echoes of those outcries
seemed to come through the death-like blackness,
yet I knew they were the phantasms of sounds and
not real repetitions.

At last morning appeared, or such faint rays of
it as could penetrate our prison. Thyra woke,
and the long sleep seemed to have restored her,
for she spoke rationally enough, though I could
hardly answer her, I was so overcome by the
horrors of the night. I wondered that she could
have been so exhausted as to have slept, and heard
nothing. But I would not tell her what I had
heard.

During that day Thyra told me something that
made me at first think that her mind wandered
again, for I could not deem her tale credible.
She told me that the Swiss Reformer, Ulrich

Zwingli, who introduced the Reformation into Zurich, and who did so much against the church of Rome, had dreadfully persecuted some Anabaptists. It seemed as if persons who had known how wickedly the church of Rome persecuted those good people called "heretics," would hardly try to turn persecutors themselves, just after having obtained their own religious freedom, but Thyra said it was so. And, alas, I fear she spoke truly! We poor Anabaptists have been persecuted by Romanists and anti-Romanists also. Neither would let us have religious freedom.

"Zwingli and his followers went so far at one time that they threw about twenty Anabaptists, men and women and children, into a dark, miserable tower," Thyra told me, "and pronounced sentence upon them that they should never see either sun or moon for the remainder of life, and should be fed till death on bread and water. And, to make the sentence more terrible it was decreed that the prisoners should stay in the dark tower together, both the living and the dead, surrounded with filth and petrefaction, until not a single one of these Anabaptists should remain alive."

"Oh, Thyra!" I exclaimed ; "Christians could not do such things to one another ! That is the way the priests and friars act to the Lollards and the gospellers ! It must be it was the church of Rome that treated those Anabaptists so."

"No," persisted Thyra, "it was the Reformer

Zwingli and his followers! Why, you have heard of that famous Anabaptist, Balthasar Hübmaier, who went to the stake a few years ago (1528), and whose wife they drowned in the river Danube?"

"Yes, surely," I answered.

"He said that those Anabaptists were treated so by Zwingli and his followers," continued Thyra. "And Balthasar Hübmaier said too that some of those Anabaptists in that dreadful tower would refuse to take even a mouthful of bread, and would not eat for three days in succession, that the other persons might have more to eat. And it was all because they were Anabaptists! Pious Christian people, of whom no one could speak any evil, except to say that they had received baptism!"

Thyra began to tell me that Zwingli knew well what the Anabaptists believe. At least he knew, she said, of their faith being that infants are unable to repent or to trust in Christ for salvation, and therefore should not receive baptism, that ordinance being for those who believe that through Christ their sins are blotted out. But another thought seemed to strike Thyra, and she began to tell me how the Anabaptist Balthasar Hübmaier himself had been put to the torture, but I turned faint and could not hear the story.

"Thyra," I begged, "stop!"

She said no more, and I lay till the wretchedly faint feeling left me. Then I sat up and leaned against the wall. By-and-by I rose and walked around the little cell. I had thought of something. How was it that those sounds had come so distinctly through the wall the night before? I had heard the man's choking and gasping, his pitiable appeals for mercy, his strangled return to breath, almost as clearly as if he had been in the same cell that we occupied. Could such a thing be, if the walls were as thick as they seemed?

"There is a loose stone somewhere, or some hole that leads into that room," I assured myself. "I will find out what it is."

Thyra watched me as I carefully felt the walls.

"Why do you do it?" she asked; but I dared not refer her mind to those sounds.

I felt over those walls all day. The occupation served to keep me from thinking how hungry I was. I almost despaired sometimes as I felt of the stones, but I prayed God to guide my fingers, and I hunted on.

It was toward evening, when down near the floor, feeling a large stone, I thought it moved slightly. I tried again. I was sure it shook.

"Thyra!" I said softly; "Thyra!"

She turned her head.

"Come and help me," I whispered. She came, wondering, but when she felt the stone move, she was as eager as I.

We tugged at the stone together or singly, as our breath held out. Gradually we pulled it out farther into our cell. When the stone was drawn so that it projected into our prison, and was toppling, Thyra and I both sat down on the floor and rested a few minutes to get breath. But the light of hope was in our faces. We smiled at each other, and it seemed strange to smile, so little cause had we had for doing so in recent days. One more pull and the stone would be out.

"The stone above this one is loose," murmured Thyra, with her hand upon the wall.

"We must not let that stone fall when we draw the lower one out," I warned. "Let us see if we can pull the upper one out first."

But we could not. The upper stone even held its place after we had dragged the lower entirely out, so wedged in was the block.

"There is a passage," I whispered, seeing amid the dust and darkness what the removal of the lower stone had revealed. "Oh, will this stone never move? Do not make a noise!"

We could not help it. The second stone we strove with was loosened now, and fell, notwithstanding all our efforts. The noise of its fall echoed in our ears, and we held our breath and looked at one another, waiting for discovery.

But no one came. Thyra and I, at last, with much exertion pulled the second stone from our way, and a narrow passage lay before us through the wall. The passage led to darkness as far as we could see, but I believed it would open into that cell where last night's horror had been enacted.

I drew a long breath.

"Come," I whispered to Thyra.

An instant more, and I was crawling through the narrow passage.

We had not gone more than a little way when I struck my forehead against something that was so cold it sent a chill through me. Yet I perceived immediately that what I had touched was nothing I need fear, being merely a piece of grating through which I could now see that there was a cell beyond. I feared lest the grating should prove so strong as to resist me and prevent us from doing anything else but to go back to our prison. But I laid hold of the grating, and it proved very old and feeble, for it bent readly before my pressure, and it was but a little while till I had broken and bent aside the obstruction.

Through this old grating I had not been able to see much of the interior of the cell, for such was the angle of the little passage in which I had crept that I could view but a small portion of the cell's floor. And my next thought, after going through the broken old grating myself, and once standing upright in this other cell, was to help Thyra out through the opening. So I did not look around till we were both in the little room.

Then Thyra half cried out in alarm, and the same instant I saw what caused her cry.

"It is the re-baptizer!" I gasped.

The faint light showed the motionless form of a man seated on the floor and leaning against the wall. His open eyes stared with the wide gaze

of the dead. His tongue protruded a little from
his mouth. There were purple marks all over his
throat, and noticeably was there a deep blotch beneath his chin.

Thyra's eyes followed the gaze of the dead
Anabaptist, upward, past us.

"He looks toward the only land where there is
religious freedom," she whispered.

There was an awfulness in the rigid, bruised
form before us. I felt a chill of fear go over me
as I looked at those fixed eyes appealing upward
to God. I heard those fiendish voices sounding
again in my ears the malignant words: "Is it
once, or is it twice? Re-baptizer, is it once or is it
twice?"

Thyra laid her hands softly on the dead man's
eyes, and sought to close them, but she could not.
He looked on through her fingers, looked on after
she had taken away her hand. And I thought
of the multitude of such martyrs whose dead eyes
also looked up to God, and whose dead lips
were set in silent appeal to him to send religious freedom to his people. Was not this dead
man before me one of God's agents in securing
that religious liberty which my father had often
said he believed would come sometime.

"Sometime, Editha, sometime, men will be
free to worship God, free to read the New Testament, without being sent to the stake."

In sight of that man who had given up his
life rather than his right to believe and prac-

tise what God's word says, I suddenly felt as I
had never felt before, what the work of the Anabaptist is.   It is to aid the coming of equal religious liberty to all.   For I felt sure that if this
Christian had been in the place of his enemies,
in power instead of captivity, he would not have
attempted to compel them by bodily attack, by
the cruelty of smiting and choking, or by threat
of the stake, to turn them to his belief.   Rather, he
would have given them the New Testament, and
asked them to search for themselves and see if
what he believed was not the command of our
Lord.

"Freedom! Freedom! That is what we want!"
my father had cried.   "Freedom of soul for every
man.   Why should a king or priest try to bind
any man's soul? What right has one man to forbid another man to worship God in liberty?"

And this had been the cry of every Anabaptist
I had ever known.   Would the Anabaptists ever
succeed in gaining what they were struggling and
praying and dying to obtain?   The God of
martyrs knew.   Earth looked dark enough.

The thin, bruised face, the rigid form, the
dreadfully appealing gaze of the dead Anabaptist's eyes, held Thyra and me awe-bound for a
few moments, forgetful of our own danger in being where we were.

"Thyra, Thyra!" I whispered, my eyes on
the purple blotches of that throat; "no Anabaptist ever treated another person in that way."

She shuddered, and stooping, touched the dead man's wrist ; it was pulseless.

"He is dead! He is dead !" she said, shivering. "Let us go away."

Where could we go ? We tried the door; it was fast. We might as well have stayed in our own cell, as far as escape was concerned. We waited, and it grew darker, darker. I could not keep my eyes from the face of the dead man, showing a faintly lighter thing through the gloom. By-and-by the cell was darker still, but I could not help fancying that I saw the dead martyr's eyes looking yet upward with their awful appeal.

CHAPTER XI

ESCAPE

"LISTEN!" whispered Thyra, grasping my arm in the dark of the night.

I had already heard. A slow, shuffling foot walked outside the cell. The sound stopped at the door. Thyra and I hastily stepped to a spot where we thought we would be behind the door when it swung open inward. This was the only protection we might have from discovery. We had no time to creep back into the passage between the two cells.

After a sound of fumbling at the fastenings, the door swung upon us. A little light from a small lamp showed faint rays in the dark, and an ugly-looking old man shuffled in. The door and the dimness of the light served to conceal us, though we shook at near discovery, as the bent, stupid-appearing visitor slowly crossed the room to the body of the Anabaptist.

The old man bent farther down with his back toward us. He was trying to unfasten the chain that bound the victim to the wall.

Thyra pulled at my hand, and silently glided from behind the door. She did not make a sound in the semi-darkness. The door was wide open.

I could not hear the faintest noise to indicate when Thyra passed over the threshold and into the corridor.

The old man rattled the chain, and made impatient mutterings and deep guttural noises, as he tried to unfasten the body that he had come to bear away.

Could I glide out as silently as Thyra had done? I drew a long breath and stealthily, with heavily beating heart, came on tiptoe from behind the door. Slowly and softly I moved toward the opening. Once let me make a sound, and what might not follow?

The old man had succeeded in unfastening the chain, and it fell with a loud rattle. Amid the noise I sped out of the door, caught Thyra's hand, and together we hurried through the dark, anywhere —anywhere to escape! We stopped after a while, for we dare not run whither we knew not. But we heard groans from what seemed to be another cell, and we hastened out of hearing. Soon we saw behind us the glimmer of a light, and the form of the old man, bending beneath the dead that he bore. He turned in another direction, and we were left in darkness again.

Now we knew not whether to congratulate ourselves that we had escaped from the cell, or not, save that we were glad to be free to move farther. For we could not tell where we were, or what was the way out of this prison, and we dared not whisper to each other, lest some hand should suddenly reach out of the dark and seize us. I was convinced that no one had gone to our cell to take cognizance of our absence, or to leave food there, or to threaten us with torture. I believed that our captors meant to starve us. And I wondered what had become of my father and my mother. Were they in some such prison as this?

Thyra and I felt softly along the walls, carefully feeling with our feet also, before taking a step. It was well we did so, for once when I put out my foot I could find no place to set it down.

Startled, I drew back, crouched on my knees, and felt before me with my hands. In front of me there seemed to be a kind of opening in the stone floor. After feeling awhile, I found that instead of the pit into which I had supposed I had been about to fall, this was a stairway that descended somewhere. I drew Thyra to me, and putting my mouth to her ear, whispered as softly as I could the fact of my discovery. She felt the stairway also, and we began to creep softly and cautiously down. For anything that we knew the stairway might be as safe for us as the corridor through which we had come. Everything was blackness.

We proceeded downward for perhaps thirty steps. Then this passage seemed to open into another one. We walked a distance, and suddenly we found ourselves in a room where a small lamp, placed on the floor, shone feebly on the face and tonsured head of a priest.

K

A thrill of fear ran over me, and then I saw that the face was that of a dying priest, of one so near death that he might do us no harm. His eyes observed us, and he seemed afraid. He shrank from us, and in a whisper begged us not to trouble him. It was not until I answered, that he seemed to realize that we were indeed human. I think, from what he afterward said, that he had thought we were some of his murdered victims.

But when he knew we were human, he caught at me with his thin, nerveless fingers, and besought us, for the love of God and Our Lady, to listen.

"I hear it! I hear it!" His faint voice rose into what was the shriek of a whisper. "I hear it night and day. Water—dripping, dripping!"

There was a cup of water beside him, and thinking he was thirsty, I offered it to him. But the dying man put it away with warding hands and a gesture of horror.

"I hear," he whispered, and his whisper had an awful alarm in it; "I hear the water dripping—dripping—dripping!"

A cold sweat stood on his face. He began rapidly, in that gasping whisper, to pour forth a confession, and afraid as we were that we might be discovered, we could not leave a dying man in such agony of soul as seemed to torment this priest.

Gradually, from his agonized whispers, I came to understand that he had been long a priest, sometimes in Spain, sometimes in England, of late years in the Low Countries. The tonsure of his head was large, indicating that he had been of rank in the church. But though the tonsure is said to represent the crown of thorns worn by Christ, I fear this priest had had little of the spirit of our Lord.

Now that he was dying, there was one crime which haunted him more than all else beside. He had helped for a time in Spain the work of the Inquisition. He had been stationed at Valladolid and elsewhere.

One dreaded torment to which the Inquisition sometimes put its victims was, this priest whispered, the binding of a person, placing him in a "groove," the feet being higher than the head. A wet, fine linen cloth was then put into the victim's mouth, and an earthen vessel was held above his face so that from a hole in the bottom of the vessel water little by little fell continuously, yet so slowly that it required an hour for a pint to thus drip away. The water fell on the nostrils and the mouth of the victim, who found it impossible to breathe, the wet linen cloth and the unnatural position combining to increase the difficulty. The result often was the rupture of some blood-vessel in the lungs of the person so tortured.

It seems that the priest, who was in gasping whispers telling us this tale, had often held the earthen vessel over the mouths and nostrils of the

condemned, and deliberately kept the water dripping, suffocating the victims. There was one
man particularly, who haunted the priest now,
one whom the priest insisted he now saw at
nights, lying in the groove.

"I can hear the water dripping, dripping, oh,
so softly dripping," he asserted. "Do you not
hear it? There! it drips, it drips."

A dreadful shuddering shook him, but Thyra
and I heard nothing like the sound which terrified
his innermost soul.

As he had told his tale, however, I had remembered him. There had been something that I recalled about his face from the first instant. I
knew now who he was. I was sure I knew.
He had said that he was once a priest in England.

He was none other than that stranger priest
who, six years before, when I had been a little
girl of ten, had accosted Stephen and me at Caversham and asked us if we knew where John Eld
lived. This was the priest I had watched through
the crevice in Neighbor Eld's hut stirring the
straw of the bed, striking here and there in the
corners of the hut, trying to find something. Woe
would have been to Neighbor Eld that day if this
man had found him.

Why was this priest left to die alone? Where
were the other priests who should now attend this
dying member of their order? Where was the
pyx, the *viaticum* for the dying? Where were

the holy candles which should have been burning about him?

"I hear," gasped once more the dying man, in a whisper shriller than before, "I hear the dripping."

Thyra bent toward him.

"Believe on the Lord Jesus Christ, and thou shalt be saved," she whispered. "Oh, cry the prayer of the penitent thief who was saved on the cross, 'Lord, remember me!'"

But the priest heeded not. He had raised his tonsured head with the strength of the dying. A hideous fear was in his face.

"I hear——" he whispered with labored breath, "I hear—the dripping—of water."

An infinite horror was looking out of his eyes.

He fell back. There was twice a twitching of his mouth dreadful to see. There was a choking sound in his throat.

Thyra caught my hand. The priest had gone to the judgment of God.

Thyra and I stood speechless; then, still clasping hands, terror-stricken, we remembered ourselves and where we were. I pointed toward a door opposite the opening where we had entered the room. Thyra and I silently reached the door and tried it. It was fastened, but we succeeded in unfastening it, not knowing what would meet us on the other side. The door opened, grating a little, and we hastily stepped through and shut it.

A cool wind struck my face. I could hardly

believe it. We stood in an archway outside the building.

It was night. The archway was blackness, but leading up before us were a few steps, and far above them I saw the sky. Thyra and I forgot all caution and ran up the steps. We fled as if for our lives. It seemed as though the face of the dead priest followed us. I ran faster at the thought, and faster still we sped when we remembered that we had left the door unfastened and we might have been heard and pursued. But I reflected that the discovery of the death of the priest would probably so excite the discoverer that he would not think to try the door to see if it was fastened.

At length we stopped in a spot beside some water. Thyra bent and drank greedily.

"I am so thirsty," she whispered.

We were hungry and thirsty both. I was almost faint for lack of food. We drank and drank of the water for which our parched mouths had so longed, and I thought of those who had been perhaps our fellow-prisoners, who were now languishing for water and were unable to get it. It seemed almost heartless for us to sit there in the darkness, drinking, washing our dusty faces, and wetting our aching heads. But discovery and re-imprisonment might come with morning. Now, at least, we were free and we had water. And yet I could hardly bear to touch the water when I remembered the priest's dying words.

"I wonder where we shall find something to eat?" whispered Thyra.

I thought, but did not say, that perhaps we would be recaptured before morning, and would be spared all further anxiety as to our eating.

Evidently some such thought passed through Thyra's mind too, for she whispered softly : "Did you hear about that Anabaptist girl here in the Hague, five years ago? She was the daughter of Weynken Claes, of Monickendam, and she was strangled and burnt.

"And this year," went on Thyra, finding that I did not answer, "nine Anabaptist citizens of Amsterdam were martyred here in the Hague. Yes, and Kraen of Harzenswovde and his wife, and two other Anabaptists were put to death at Haarlem, where Jan Walen and two companions were strangled and burnt, I believe, as that girl was I told you about, the daughter of Weynken Claes."

"Thyra," I answered in a whisper, "do not talk. I am afraid some one will hear."

But she was too much agitated to be quiet.

"I cannot understand it," she whispered on. "The Anabaptists are always persecuted, always. Whoever writes the history of the Anabaptists will write it in blood and tears. Why is it that we are persecuted above all other people?"

Now I remembered that once when my aunt had been speaking to my father, during the time that we two families had lived in the same boat, she having in spite of her prejudice observed the good character of the Anabaptists, had asked him this self-same question.

"But why," my aunt had persisted, "why do they suffer so? I cannot understand it."

My father drew a quick breath, and his cheeks flushed.

"I can tell you," he answered. "It is because we hold the truth."

"Other sects claim the same for themselves," objected my aunt.

"But none hold it as we," asserted my father, his eagerness flashing forth in his face. "None as we. We take our baptism from the plain word of the New Testament, not from any word of priest, or pope, or council. Search and look if it is not so. Search and look if the New Testament says not that one must repent and be baptized. Can a babe repent? Then wherefore should it be baptized? Search and look if the New Testament says not that our Lord came up out of the water after his baptism, and that we are buried with him in baptism. Is sprinkling a burial? Do you not know that we Anabaptists have more of the truth than others, because we hold more closely the New Testament? That is the reason we are so persecuted. Yea, but our persecutions will work out the religious freedom of ourselves and all other men. So I hope and believe."

It was this that I remembered, and told Thyra, and she grew glad in the thought.

"Oh," she said, "if one could but think that! If one could be sure that all this agony would end at last in religious freedom for all men, then how happy we might be that the Lord has accounted us worthy to suffer most, not only for his sake, but for the sake of human beings."

"Will not God hear his people?" I whispered. "Surely all their prayers for religious freedom will not be in vain."

I could not think what Thyra and I would better do. Perhaps we could find our way back to the *treckschuyt* where my father, my mother, and I had been surprised and taken. It seemed a dangerous way to go, but I felt a sudden hope, and my heart beat quickly at the thought that possibly my father and my mother might have escaped in some way from their captors, and might have gone back to the *treckschuyt*, and be waiting and hungering for my coming. I half persuaded myself that it might be so. In a quiver of excitement I told Thyra what I thought, and asked her if she dared go with me, or if she thought our enemies would find us there.

She was very doubtful what to say. Finally, we left the place where we had been hiding, and went silently down a street. How should we know where we were? We came upon a little, low, black tower, hanging apparently over the waters of a marsh. What was this place? We turned and passed down another street. We disturbed a stork, and were afraid of the consequences, but the bird merely moved a little. We wandered on, we knew not where, and came upon a scaffold. Shuddering at what it implied, we hurried away. The hours of darkness were going by. What should we do if morning came without our escaping from the city?

We found a canal and followed it for a distance. A saltness began to be felt faintly in the air. We must be going in the right direction, for that odor came from the sea. It was in that direction on the canal that the *treckschuyt* lay, or had lain. Thyra and I crept under a gate, and hurried further down the canal. By-and-by, when we had walked awhile, I became sure of our direction. I had seen this way before.

"Come," I hastened Thyra.

We ran.

There at last, through the trees that bordered the canal, we saw the black outline of the old *treckschuyt*, moored still close to the side of the canal path. Thyra and I softly rushed toward the boat. We clambered on board with caution, being mindful of the fact that some of our enemies might have taken possession. Morning was coming, and we must have some place to hide.

Softly we looked into the compartment of the *treckschuyt* next the prow. I was trembling with excitement. What if in one of these compartments I should find the two over whose unknown fate I had spent such hours of agonizing speculation, my father and my mother?

But by the dim light everything seemed to be in the same semi-confusion in which we had left the boat. Things remained where they had been dropped. This sent all hope from me. I burst into tears. Thyra sympathizingly suggested that we look into the other compartment.

"Do not give up hope, Editha," she whispered, her arms around me. "They may be safe, even if they are not here."

But, though I followed Thyra, I could not keep from tears. The other compartment we found to be in order. Nothing had been touched. Here was where we had hidden the copy of the New Testament. I uncovered the hiding-place, and at the sight of the treasured book that had accompanied us through so many perils I gave way altogether. Thyra held me in her arms till my sobbing ceased. The faint light of morning came in upon us sitting there desolate.

When I looked up at last and saw the tears on the cheeks of my friend, I realized how selfish I had been. Thyra had sorrows too. She did not know whether her brother was alive or dead. He was two years older than Thyra, and had been away from home on an errand at the time that the onset was made by the persecutors on Thyra's family. Their boat-home had been burned, and the old grandfather killed. Thyra, the brother, and the grandfather had comprised the family, for the father and the mother of my friend had been dead for years. Thyra had now no place to go to.

It was well I could bring her here to the *treck-schuyt*.

If I had known where my aunt and Stephen were I might, perhaps, have communicated with them. But my aunt now made a living by carrying on her own large boat, produce to and from the markets. Stephen was becoming a great traveler and a shrewd worker, who, with the assistance of a big dog, managed to keep pulling the large boat along as the two trotted beside the canals. My aunt could stay on board and act as steerswoman. Between them, she and her son made a comfortable living. Where they were now I did not know. Whether they had heard of our calamity I very much doubted. Probably my aunt's boat had not passed here since the night of our capture.

Morning came, but we dared not show ourselves on the boat, and so remained hidden. I showed Thyra where we kept our eatables and our drinking water. We took some bread and cheese, and ate with tears.

" Oh, Thyra, Thyra ! " I cried, " if only we knew where they all are, your brother, and my father and my mother, we would go away with them from this dreadful country. But how can we go away and leave them? We should never know what became of them. "

And we sobbed together.

So the sad day went by. We could look out at the canal, and once I saw a boat loaded with peat

and towed by a man, a woman, and a child, one
behind another, with a cord attached to a sort of
leather band. And once, another boat went by
towed by a man, helped by a large dog. But no
one came near to disturb our *treckschuyt*. We
read some in the New Testament, and I told
Thyra how my father used to hide with the book
in the fagot pile. Thyra said she thought her
brother had had with him a copy of the New Testament, which was, of course, in Dutch, although
Thyra and he could read and talk both Dutch and
English.

We watched diligently for any appearance of
my aunt's boat, and Thyra and I talked of the
horrors of the Spanish Inquisition, which the
emperor seemed to wish to bring upon the Low
Countries. Thyra knew more than I upon the
subject, although I had heard horrors enough, and
the ghastly remembrances that had looked from
the dying priest's eyes were fresh in my mind.
But Thyra told me of the horrible tortures that
the Spanish Inquisition was accustomed to inflict
on its victims. At midnight, she said, in some
dungeon, the executioner, who was covered from
head to foot with a black robe, and whose eyes
glared through holes cut in the hood that muffled
his face, would torture a victim with every form
of agony the monks had been able to invent; by
water, by weights, by pulleys, by screws, by the
rack. The victim was often not tormented to
death, but was saved for unlimited periods of tor-

ture. Thyra told me that she had heard of persons who had borne the torture and the Spanish
dungeon for fifteen years, and at last had been
burned at the stake. For, if a confession was
wrung from a victim under torture, the result was
not release, but burning. There was no escape. If
a priest himself was a victim, before he was burned
his hands, lips, and shaven crown were scraped
with a piece of glass, by which act the oil of his
consecration was supposed to be removed. Then
he was put in with the other victims, and all
mounted the scaffold, and were delivered by the
inquisitors into the hands of the executioner.
The inquisitors, on handing him the prisoners,
would make a sarcastic request that he would deal
tenderly with them without blood-letting or injury. If a victim remained steadfast to the last,
he was burned alive. But if he renounced his
faith, he was first strangled.

My heart seemed to die within me at Thyra's
words. What awful thing might not be done to
those dearest to me? What might they not
already have endured?

"Perish the Inquisition!" the dying priest had
whispered fiercely.

Oh, that so foul an institution should lay its
hand on the Low Countries! Oh, that we were
not bound to Spain!

"Do you know," said Thyra to me, "that people say that St. Dominic was the founder of the
Inquisition?"

St. Dominic. He was a saint very familiar to me, for my aunt had often told me of him and his marvelous deeds; that often he floated in the air before the eyes of his disciples; that the most intense flames would not burn the parchment upon which were written the divine meditations of this saint; that once when Dominic was standing in the midst of a pious throng in the convent of St. Sixtus, talking with the Cardinal Stephen, a messenger, weeping, came to announce that the nephew of Stephen had been thrown from his horse, and lay dead at the gate of the convent.

The Cardinal Stephen overcome, fell weeping on Dominic, and the compassionate saint ordered that the body of the dead young man should be brought in. Dominic commanded the altar to be arranged for celebrating mass; he fell into an ecstasy, and as he touched the sacred elements he rose in air, and hung kneeling in the empty space above the astonished spectators. He came down and made the sign of the cross over the dead; he ordered the young man to arise, and the dead sprang up, alive and well, in sight of the witnesses around; so they said.

So it was this saint who was reputed to have founded that thing of blood, the Spanish Inquisition, this "Holy Office" which was to devour the Low Countries.

"Oh," I answered Thyra, "it cannot be; it cannot be that the Emperor Charles will want to kill so many of us!"

Little did I know the Emperor Charles. Little did I know the excess of cruelty to which a devoted bigot may go, under a mistaken idea of what will please God. Neither could I look forward at the coming years, and see the Low Countries deluged with Anabaptist blood, shed in the name of religion, because Charles V. thought that what he was pleased to call "heresy" should be destroyed. I did not know that Charles' grandmother Isabella, who had been persuaded to let the Inquisition rage in Spain, had said: "In the love of Christ and his maid-mother, I have caused great misery, and have depopulated towns and districts, provinces and kingdoms."

A strange thing to do for the "love of Christ," one would think. How little can those who are guided by the priests know what will please our Lord! I did not know that Charles V., our emperor, regretted that he had ever kept his word to Luther and allowed him to depart in safety, when he had had a chance to kill that good man. It was well I could not look forward at the future years of Charles' power over the Low Countries, and then on to the reign of his son Philip. It was he, who once, when there was a great burning of victims at Valladolid, in Spain, was accosted by one Carlos de Sessa, a young nobleman of distinguished character who was about to suffer, and who passing by the throne to the stake, said to the king: "How can you thus look on, and permit me to be burned?"

And Philip had made answer, "I would carry
the wood to burn my own son withal, were he as
wicked as you."

Small hope might any "heretic" of the Low
Countries have of life, if he fell into the hands of
either Charles or his son. And an Anabaptist was
counted the worst kind of heretic.

The day went by and Thyra and I were not
molested on board the old *treckshuyt*. The night
came. Thyra was distressed and restless, and I
felt so sorrowful and uneasy I could not sleep.
How could either of us sleep, not knowing what
was happening in the Hague? The night hours
passed as silently as the waters of the canal. I
lay still, hoping that Thyra slept, but on my
drawing a long breath once she sighed also, and I
knew she was awake.

"Perhaps to-morrow my aunt may come," I whispered; "though she is of the Romish belief still."

But Thyra only sobbed.

A little while after this we heard somebody
softly come on board. Whoever the person was,
he did not come into the compartment of the
treckschuyt where we were hidden. Soon there
were muffled voices, and Thyra and I tremblingly
felt the old *treckschuyt* begin to move through
the water. The boat was evidently being towed
somewhere by some people who thought that the
Anabaptist family had been exterminated and
would never need the *treckschuyt* again.

What should we do? Where were we going?
The old *treckschuyt* moved very quietly.
Driven desperate at last I crept to the door, and
peered out. Everything else was so still that I
could hear the rustle of the sails of a windmill
on shore. I discovered that there were some six
men on board. Four of them appeared to be
prisoners, over whom another man held guard
while the sixth man managed the helm. A rope
stretched from the iron ring under the prow and
ended off somewhere in the dark, I knew on
shore. Perhaps the *treckschuyt* was being towed
by men, perhaps by a horse ridden by a man.
Our boat passed along like a shadow among
shadows.

"We are going back to the Hague," I concluded. "I do not believe it is safe there for us."

I crept back to Thyra.

"If we could slip out and get our little boat,"
I whispered, "we might lower it and float away,
if we could do it without being seen."

But we dared not attempt this. Moreover, at
that moment, the *treckschuyt* stopped, and three
more men, prisoners also, appeared on board.

Now, indeed, we saw certainly that we could
not obtain the small boat without attracting attention. And so once more we passed on up to the
Hague.

At the landing the men all left the *treckschuyt*.
From the low remarks we had caught, we were
sure that the three prisoners who had last come

on board were Anabaptists, for the guard had mockingly spoken to them as " Re-baptizers," and had threatened to throw them, chained together as they were, into the canal. Also, from something the steersman had said, we learned that it was probable that the old *treckschuyt* would be used hereafter for the conveying of those heretics who were on their way to prison. That was the last thing I learned before the men went ashore.

Thyra and I felt, therefore that we had little time in which to abandon the *treckschuyt*. We let down the small boat, put in it what provisions we had, together with some clothing, stepped aboard and pushed off softly in the dark. But no one need think that I had left the New Testament behind in the old *treckschuyt*. That dear book I had safely with me.

We rowed a short distance softly, lest one of the men might come back to the *treckschuyt* and hear us. Then, when we thought we were far enough away, having tied a rope to our boat, Thyra guided it to land and she and I stepped ashore in the dark, and hand in hand ran, towing the boat. Our only desire was to rush as far away from the *treckschuyt* as possible. And yet as I ran along the canal-path, my heart turned back to the Hague. Had I dared I would have wished we were running the other way to enter the Hague and to search every building of that city to find those for whom Thyra and I so sorely longed. Alas! What had become of them?

Once in a while we stopped and panted for breath, and looked fearfully behind us, ready to abandon everything and flee to the shadow of the trees by the canal if we thought we were pursued. Though Thyra declared that if anybody tried to drown her in the canal, according to the threat of the men to the Anabaptist captives on board the *treckschuyt*, it would be discovered that she could swim well. And when I asked her if she supposed that many Anabaptists had been drowned, she answered that in Zurich, two years ago, there was an edict published which made it death for any to baptize by immersion, and under this law some Anabaptists had been tied back to back and thrown so into the water. Then I remembered that my father had once told me of this same thing.

"Where shall we go?" Thyra asked me abruptly.

And I answered: "Let us go and hide away in the sand dunes, toward the village of Scheveningen."

Without a word, Thyra drew the boat to land. We took our bundles and cast the boat adrift. We turned our faces toward the direction of Scheveningen and hurried away, though we could not run so fast as we had before, because now we had our bundles to carry, though they were not very heavy.

By-and-by we came to a place where a desert of sand suddenly seemed to stretch before us. A continuous murmur of the sea was on the salt air. We had reached the dunes. Toiling over and around one hillock of sand after another we walked for a while, and then so weary that we could hardly keep awake, we asked the protection of the Lord, and lay down in a hollow surrounded by the hillocks of sand, where we soon slept, though I could hardly realize yet that we were out in the world and not confined in prison. I had little hope but that we should speedily be retaken.

CHAPTER XII

EDITHA'S EXPERIENCE

IT was morning when I awoke, and Thyra was still asleep. I sat up, and looked around me. Overhead was a gray sky. On all sides of me rose yellow hills of sand, from thirty to forty feet high, or a little more. I crept to the top of one, and peered cautiously out. I saw no person, but the hillocks made the region seem almost mountainous. There were three ranges of dunes, and they hindered one from seeing over the flats. The hillocks also prevented me from seeing the village of Scheveningen, excepting its church spire.

I slid down from my hillock as Thyra awoke. We stayed in our place of refuge all day. Toward evening we spied a woman of Scheveningen striding along with a cart drawn by two great dogs. She had been to the Hague to sell fish and was going home. Thyra and I, from behind a hillock, watched her, and I know wished that we also had a home to go to.

The woman wore a queer hat of straw, a brownish-colored mantle lined with red, a white skirt, white wooden shoes, and walked with long strides.

"I wonder if we dare trust her?" I whispered to Thyra.

She did not know. We stayed again that night
among the yellow dunes, and we finished the last
of our provisions. Early the next morning we
saw the same woman striding by with a basketful
of fish on her head. We watched her.

"She has a good face," commented Thyra.
"Can you talk the dialect of Scheveningen!"

"No," I answered.

"Neither can I," confessed Thyra, regretfully.
"Perhaps she may understand Dutch. Let us
watch for her when she comes back, and speak to
her. I do not believe she will harm us. And we
must do something. Our food is gone."

It was several hours before the woman returned.
We had seen two or three of the other inhabitants of Scheveningen pass carrying fish; but we
preferred to wait for our fish-selling woman.

When she passed us, we called to her, and although she could talk with us but little, she
seemed to understand our Dutch, and to comprehend what our trouble was. She beckoned us to
follow her, and guided us through the ranges of
dunes till at last we came to the village of Scheveningen.

There she went with us up a narrow lane to a
house, said to a woman there, "Doopsgezinden,"
(Baptists), and then left us. Our new friend, who
was very grave and dignified, as are all the inhabitants of Scheveningen, kindly gave us food, and
seemed to wish to be most hospitable. She was
able to understand Dutch, and we told her all our

story without reserve. In return she showed a place where we might live as long as we wished, she said, and Thyra and I entreated her to ask any of the Scheveningen women whom she could trust, to search when they visited the Hague, and see if they could at all discover what had become of my father and mother and Thyra's brother. Also I besought her to look for the coming of my aunt's boat to the Hague, for Thyra and I did not dare to go to that city.

All this the woman kindly promised to do, and I, who afterward heard her singing what I knew to be a Psalm, felt no more fear of her. We found that the people of Scheveningen generally were grave and devout. They had their Bibles, their hymns, their Psalms. We could hardly have discovered a place where we would have felt more safe, even though our surroundings seemed strange. Thyra and I stayed closely at home, but we helped the women all we could with their fish and their household duties, for we did not wish to be burdensome. And we waited, oh, how anxiously we waited, every day for news from the Hague! Thyra grew thin with watching and waiting and grief, and I could not comfort her, being too spent with the dreadful anxiety myself.

For at any hour news might come, and we started at every sound not so much for fear of recapture as for thinking who might be coming. Some of the fish-selling women I knew were trying as well as they could to gain information for us. And yet day after day the women would come in, and Thyra and I would look hastily to see if news had come, and each woman would shake her head.

But one day there came to the cottage a woman who rushed to me, and caught me in her arms, crying: "My child! my poor child!"

It was not my mother. It was my aunt, and we sobbed together, till looking up, I saw Stephen.

Oh, it seemed almost like home again to see them both! But my aunt was wild with fear over my mother's fate.

"Oh, if your father had let that New Testament alone, we might all have been living safely home in Caversham," she wailed, wringing her hands. "See what trouble that book has brought."

My aunt urged that we go back with her to her large boat. She wanted me near her, and declared that Stephen and she would conceal us.

"Come, you and Thyra both," she urged.

At first I thought perhaps we would go. But when my aunt spied among my things the New Testament, her face changed.

"Did you save *that?*" she asked. "I thought you had left that book on board the *treckschuyt.*"

"I would not have left our New Testament behind," I answered quietly. "We Anabaptists love the New Testament."

My aunt stood, hesitating, perplexed.

"Editha," she said, at last, "I would be glad to have you and Thyra on our boat, but I cannot risk my life for your ideas. You know the edict of the emperor is that there must be no reading of the Scriptures in the Low Countries. Leave the New Testament here. It has done harm enough already. And above all things leave your Anabaptist ideas."

I looked at Stephen, but he avoided my gaze. He knew well enough what good the New Testament had done. I was persuaded that he had not forgotten those days when he read the word in our *treckschuyt*, and when he thought he became a Christian. But his mother's influence was strong upon him now. I looked at my aunt.

"I cannot leave the New Testament," I replied. "I think perhaps Thyra and I would better stay here, after all; for we are both Anabaptists, and it might bring trouble upon you to have us with you."

And after some persuasion, my aunt left us. For she desired to be at the Hague to search for my mother.

My aunt was kind and thoughtful too, for she made Thyra and me take from her purse some little money, and told us that she and Stephen would search for Thyra's brother too.

And him they did find. One day toward evening Thyra looking out, saw a young man running through the yellow sand dunes, and she cried: "Oh, Gaspar! Gaspar!" and flew to meet him.

Stephen had found Thyra's brother wandering disconsolately, thinking his sister dead as well as his grandfather. And Stephen had sent the young man immediately to Scheveningen.

How happy Thyra was after that! It is true she and Gaspar missed the dear old grandfather, but they knew he was safe in heaven. They had no one on earth to be anxious for, as I had. Though their boat-home was gone, Gasper and she could make another home for themselves, and they soon did so in a little cottage in Scheveningen, taking me in with them. And Gaspar risked many times going to the Hague and trying to discover some clue that would lead to news concerning my father and my mother. But though he spent much time, he brought me no news. Neither could Stephen and my aunt find out anything, though they spent money and searched for months. And I myself went to the Hague, and hunted in vain, regardless of danger. At last my aunt gave up all hope, and went away in her boat with Stephen. She offered to take me too, if I would leave the New Testament behind, but I could not, and Thyra and Gaspar said they wanted me, and I still kept hoping that possibly I might hear something if I waited long enough. So I stayed in Scheveningen, going to the Hague as often as I dared.

And the days came and went among the small, black cottages of that village. Gaspar became one of the fishermen for herring, and went away with the fleet every June, and Thyra and I stayed in the village where only women and chil-

dren were left in the fishing season. And the
boats would come back, and in some families
there would be joy and in some grief. Some of
the fishermen would never return, for the sea held
its dead.

But Gaspar always came back safely. And because I could not bear to burden Thyra and him
with my grief, I used to wander out among the
thinly grassed sand dunes when my work was done,
and there by myself I would hide, and sob, and pray,
and sometimes read my English New Testament.
But more often I could not see to read because of
my tears. For it seemed to me that my heart
would break when I thought that perhaps during
these many months my father and my mother
were kept and tortured. I used to wake in the
night shaking with horror, thinking of what might
be happening during the dark hours, and I would
cry in agony, "O God, grant that my father
and my mother may have been killed the night
they were taken prisoners rather than kept tortured till now." I would try to sleep, and would
dream that I saw my father or my mother enduring some dreadful torture of which I had
heard the dying priest speak.

And the heart-aching months went on. Three
1535 years had gone by, and one day when I
A.D. was out among those sand dunes nearest
the water, looking at the melancholy sea, shadowed by the dense clouds, Gaspar came striding
through the heavy sand, and sat down beside me.

At first he did not say anything, for he had seen the tears on my face, though I wiped them away hastily enough.

So we sat there on the sand dune, with the sound of the surge of the sea in our ears, and my heart beat heavily, for I knew why he had come.

We had sat quite a while gazing out at the restless green waters and at the misty horizon, when he turned and looked me in the face and said earnestly, "Editha, away beyond this sea lies England."

"Yes," I answered.

"And many Anabaptists are thinking of crossing over from the Low Countries to England, and making homes there," he continued. "It cannot be worse there than it is here. King Henry cannot be worse than the Emperor Charles. He means to kill all the Anabaptists in the the Low Countries. I have been thinking for some time of going to England."

And then he stopped.

"I have stayed here," he went on. Then he broke off and looked at the sea.

And finally he turned to me, with the color flushing through all his weather-beaten, manly face.

"I cannot go to England without you," he said. "Home would not be home without you, Editha; dear Editha, do you love me as I love you?"

And in the hearts of those two Anabaptists among the yellow dunes, there was a happiness

that the Emperor Charles could not, with all his
edicts, take away.

But I could not promise Gaspar to go to England. It would seem like giving up all hope of
ever hearing of my father and my mother again
if I went so far away.

But Gaspar reminded me: "It has been three
years since it all happened. Three years, Editha;
do you still hope?"

There was a great and tender pity in his voice,
so that the tears came again to my eyes, but I replied: "Oh, Gaspar, I cannot go! I cannot go!
I must see if I cannot find them."

And Gaspar did not urge me, though he affirmed: "Editha, you will never cease to grieve
as long as you live here, so near where it all happened."

But I told him that England would be a prison
for me, since I should always be thinking of the
Hague and wishing to go searching there.

"I know," he replied kindly, "I know."

And he said no more about it, but we went
home together, and I had never before thought
that the way across the dunes could be a happy
one, so often had I trodden it weary at heart and
anguished at that one idea I always carried in my
brain: "Shall I ever find them? Shall I ever find
them again?"

As for Thyra, my cousin Stephen came often
through the sand dunes, and I was not so stupid
as to think he wished to see me. But when I

spoke once jestingly to her about him, Thyra flushed and looked me straight in the eyes, and said resolutely : " Let your cousin Stephen prove himself a man who dares live what he believes, or else I will never be his wife. He knows that we Anabaptists are right. He has not forgotten the reading of the New Testament in your *treckschuyt;* and yet he dares not come out and be one of us. His mother holds him to the Roman church. She took his Dutch New Testament and sunk it in the canal. He is grown old enough to have a man's will, and yet he fears the persecution to which he knows the Anabaptists are doomed. Let him show himself a man since he believes himself a Christian. Let him obey the command of Christ and be baptized. If Stephen dare not do that, then he may learn that an Anabaptist girl will never marry a coward."

Her eyes flashed with indignation as she spoke, and I surmised that Stephen had already heard some such remarks from her. Therefore I thought he deserved to be told the plain truth, and I knew that he would feel it more from Thyra's lips than from mine. Yet I felt sure that Thyra did not look upon my winsome cousin with disfavor. If women like Thyra and the multitude of others who held the Anabaptist faith could brave death in a horrible form for their obedience to God's Word, what was Stephen indeed but a coward if he refused to be baptized when his conscience told him that he ought so to acknowledge Christ.

I came upon the two, one evening, when Thyra was reading aloud from her Testament. Stephen's head was bent on his hands as he listened. I caught sight of the heading of Thyra's page, which was Mark 1 : 10: "And straightway coming up out of the water, he saw the heavens opened, and the Spirit like a dove descending upon him."

I knew that my cousin Stephen was likely to hear some things he would remember, so I slipped away, and left those two dear young people to their discussion. If Stephen had been unconvinced of the truth of Anabaptist doctrine, the situation would have been different. But he had read God's word. He knew the truth, and did it not. He thought himself a Christian. Why should he shrink from baptism?

"I am glad that Gaspar is not like Stephen," I congratulated myself under my breath. "If the Anabaptists gain religious freedom for themselves and for others, it will only be as staunch defenders of the doctrines of God's word, not as cowards."

I went to the Hague often in these days, but I discovered nothing. And another year passed, and still there was no news, and Gaspar said to me : "It is four years. Will you go?"

At first I thought I would, for hope had died in me that I should ever see my father or my mother again. But when it occurred to me that after I had gone to England perhaps some day my father might escape from prison, and come out an almost

helpless cripple, from the torture he had endured,
or I might find that my mother, maimed, broken,
had obtained release, and I had not been near to
meet her, I cried out: "Oh, Gaspar, Gaspar, I
cannot go! I can never go away from here.

He looked very sober for a moment, and 1536
then he answered quietly: "It shall be as A.D.
you say, Editha."

So it was settled that in a few weeks we would
be married and would still stay in Scheveningen.
And yet, I trembled when I thought that it was
my word that would keep us in the Low Countries where the persecutors' hearts were fierce.
Queen Dowager Mary of Hungary, sister of the
emperor, had written to her brother, three years
before this, that in her opinion "all heretics,
whether repentant or not, should be prosecuted
with such severity as that error might be at once
extinguished, care only being taken that the
provinces were not entirely depopulated."

With this merciful limitation, a whole system
of murder was planned. In 1535 an imperial
edict was issued at Brussels, condemning all heretics to death. If a man repented he was to be
killed with the sword. If a woman repented, she
was to be buried alive. If a man or a woman persisted in being a heretic, he or she was to be
burned.

Moreover there was especially great trouble in
store for us, for there had been, in 1535, an up-
rising at Münster, charged by our enemies to the

Anabaptists, and we were looked upon as being the most dreadful sinners. The blackest misrepresentation and the sharpest punishment were to be ours.

And yet think how devout a man, in the eyes of the priests, our Emperor Charles was! He heard mass every day. Every Sunday and every holiday he listened to a sermon, and he confessed and received the sacrament four times a year. Sometimes at midnight he would be kneeling before a crucifix. In Lent he ate no meat, and was extraordinarily diligent in trying to discover and punish any man, no matter what his station, who did not fast through all Lent's forty days. So, I suppose, he thought to serve and please God, Our Lady, and the saints.

Yet it seemed hard that we, who tried to serve God according to his word, should be denounced and called "Münsterites," that name of shame which was to cling to us for so many years. And, alas! it was not only those of the church of Rome who continued to be our enemies, but it was those opposed to Rome who joined hands with the enemies of God against the Anabaptists! Where was the religious liberty we craved for all men?

Yet, sometimes when it seemed hardest that we should be so persecuted, I remembered my father's words: "Do you not know that we Anabaptists have more of the truth than others, because we hold more closely to the New Testament? That is the reason we are so persecuted! Yea, but our persecution will work out the religious freedom, not only of ourselves, but of all other men. So I hope and believe."

It was in this year we heard news from England. Sir Thomas More, he who wrote so bitterly against Tyndale, and who issued that declaration against all English translations of the Scriptures, was dead. He had been beheaded. Truly he had not found King Henry's favor very lasting. I remembered how angry I had felt with Sir Thomas More on the day when I, in rash defiance, climbed the fagot heap by daylight and boldly dropped myself down into the big hole, and there read the New Testament. Sir Thomas More had gone to give his account to God now, and Tyndale, the translator of the New Testament into English, had also gone; for an English student, Henry Phillips, had by base treachery betrayed Tyndale into the hands of the emperor's officers at Brussels. King Henry of England was, of course, anxious that Tyndale should be convicted, and, after eighteen months of imprisonment in the castle of Vilvoorden, near Brussels, the translator of our English Testament was strangled and burnt at the stake. And, just before he died, he prayed: "O Lord, open the King of England's eyes!"

John Frith, he who was Tyndale's friend, and who had been one of that band of students once shut in the fish-cellar at Oxford for reading the New Testament, was dead now also. For he, having been invited to return to England from

the continent whither he had fled, came trustingly
back, and was taken.   He was put into the stocks
at Reading, not so very far from our old home at
Caversham.   Afterward he was committed to the
Tower, and was burned to death.   So all three of
these men, Sir Thomas More, Tyndale, and John
Frith, had gone to give their account to God.

When I thought of the multitudes of people
who had suffered since we left England, my heart
misgave me whether it was better to stay in the
Low Countries, or to return to King Henry's
realm.   For it was terrible in England soon after
we left !   The bishops filled their prisons with
countless victims.   People were racked, tortured,
imprisoned, for believing that the bread of the
communion is not the real body of Christ, or for
teaching their children or reading to their neighbors a chapter of the New Testament, or for having a New Testament in their possession.

Such things had been in England since we left,
and the same king yet reigned there.   I had lived
in England, and I could not feel sure that we
should be safe if we went back ; for the hand of
both Romanist and Protestant was against the
Anabaptists, and it seemed as though few besides
us believed in religious liberty.

So in these days I lived in a strange mixture
of happiness and fear.   I wondered that I, who
had thought life was over for me, and that nothing more remained but long, heart-breaking searching and waiting for those dear ones who never

came, should feel so happy as I always did when
Gaspar was with me. Not that I forgot the fate
of my father and my mother, or that I longed and
sorrowed less for them, but a new joy had entered
my heart, and the world was different to me in
spite of the emperor and his bloody edicts.

It lacked but a week of my intended marriage
day, when I and two other women, while at the
fish-market in the Hague, were suddenly apprehended by some of the soldiery, and immediately
taken to prison. The two other women were accused of being heretics, but I, as an Anabaptist,
was to be treated with more speedy severity than
they. I was bound, and two soldiers were instructed to bury me alive when night should come.
In vain I protested that this punishment was for
those who recanted, and I, not having denied my
faith should, according to law, be reserved to be
burnt at the stake.

This I said to them, partly because I would not
be thought by any to have denied my faith, for
indeed I had not done so, and partly because I
hoped that some of the other Scheveningen
women who were in the fish-market at the time
of my arrest, would tell Gaspar and Stephen what
had befallen me, and possibly they might be able
to devise some way of helping me, if only my
death might be delayed.

But my protestations availed nothing. There
were two hours yet before sunset, and though I
was not afraid to die, life and love are sweet to

the young, and I wished that we had fled to England.

"But all that is over," I thought, as I waited for the night that would bring the execution of my dreadful sentence. "I go to-night to a better country than England. I go to a land of freedom forevermore!"

My taking and imprisonment had been accomplished so suddenly that I could hardly realize my situation. I hoped that after I was dead Gaspar would flee from this blood-stained land, and not linger here trying to discover what had become of me, as I before had stayed attempting to find out what had been my parents' doom, till too late.

At night I found myself led out to die, and a number of soldiers conducted me in grim silence without the city. There was darkness, save for the few lights that the men carried. Having marched some distance a halt was made, and two men speedily dug a deep hole, into which I was lowered, bound and helpless as I was. I had expected to be fastened into a coffin-shaped receptacle, but I was put in my grave without such ceremony. I stood upright, since there was a great sufficiency of room. One man was left to bury me. The other soldiers hurried away, for there were certain heretics that were to be apprehended, if possible, that night, a clue to their whereabouts having been supposed to be found.

The man in whose charge I was left began to shovel in the dirt upon me. I called to him, and begged him to release me, but he made no answer. I besought him with all the energy of which I was capable to help me and not kill me.

"If you would not wish my blood on your soul in that day when you will stand face to face with God, I adjure you let me go free," I implored him. "I have done no wrong."

But the man did not reply. The earth fell leisurely at first. Tug as I might at my bonds, straining every muscle, I could not release myself. I had been bound too securely. Then at last I gave up all hope of escape.

I remembered the dead Anabaptist of years before. I seemed to see his face again in the dark, his eyes looking up with their mute appeal to the God of freedom.

"My blood will also cry out unto God," I said to myself. "O God, see—see what thy people, the Anabaptists, suffer! We die, O Lord! Wilt thou not send freedom to the earth? O God, see the tears, the groans, the agony, the blood of thy servants, the Anabaptists, who have followed the precepts of thy word. Hear our prayer, O God, and send religious freedom to all men."

The earth fell regularly and swiftly upon me. I could feel the wind of its coming, and instantly the force of the earth as it fell. Now the earth was almost up to my knees. Now it was higher, so that I could just begin feel the accumulating mass with the tips of my fingers, as my hands hung bound at my sides. The earth was being

shoveled in so fast that I had to turn my head to
get breath. I glanced at the sky, saw it an instant through the small lumps of falling earth,
and then shut my eyes tightly to avoid particles
of the soil.

"That is the last time I shall look at the sky
with these eyes," I thought. "It cannot take
long to die. Only a few minutes more, and I
shall be in heaven. Dear Lord, I am not afraid
to go where I shall see thee. Oh, my Master, thou
art with me now."

The earth had reached my elbows. My arms
were absolutely immovable, as were my feet, held
by the heavy pressure of earth on them.

"I shall see father and mother," I thought.
"I am almost sure they are dead, and if they are,
I shall see them in a few minutes. Oh, I shall be
so glad to see them! I shall——"

A shovelful of earth struck me almost directly
in the face. The earth was higher, beginning to
press on my chest. The weight seemed to drive
the breath out of my lungs. I appeared to myself to breathe, but little below my throat. A
choking sensation oppressed me. The earth rose
to one shoulder. The pressure seemed to send so
much blood to my head that I grew dizzy. A
ring, Gaspar's ring, that I wore on one hand,
scorched my finger as if with molten fire. The
ring seemed to burn into my flesh, so heavy was
the pressure upon my hand. A few more shovelfuls of earth, and the work of my executioner

would be done. When he too came to die, would my face, looking out of the dark of this pit of death, haunt him, as that suffocated man's face had troubled the dying priest.

I gasped and panted for breath. I could not move save my neck and jaws and eyelids. I tried to get breath and yet not open my lips, so fearful was I that some of the falling earth might fill my mouth. A horrible dread of suffocation seized me. I could not endure it. I would not recant. No, no, it was not that! But to smother, to gasp, to choke, to suffocate.

I struggled to move, but my feet and my hands could not stir. The earth came faster. I dared not waste my breath to scream. It would do no good. I had not the strength anyway. The earth rose over my neck, to my chin. Two shovelfuls of earth fell on my head. The earth rose higher, higher. My head would soon be covered. I managed to turn it a little to one side. My mouth opened The earth fell in. I tried to eject it. I succeeded. I gasped. Some earth fell. My head seemed on fire. My mouth wanted to open again. I kept it shut. Through some great, dim distance of space, I heard a noise, a voice, a struggle. My mouth wanted to open. I held it shut. It wanted to open. It would open. It should not. It *did* open. The earth fell in.

"This is death," I thought.

I felt myself try to shut my mouth. The earth was there. Faintly I felt the groping of a hand that caught my hair. I felt hands that tore at the earth about my neck, that dug furiously at the soil. And far, far, oh, infinitely far away, was a voice that came, whether from time or eternity I did not know : "Editha! my Editha! Live a little longer! Editha! Editha! My Editha!"

I could not understand. Everything was very far away. But by-and-by, through the mist of unconsciousness, I began to feel that for some reason the earth on my chest did not oppress me any more. And then I gradually came to know that there was no earth there. Then I felt that I was being somehow dug out of my burial place, but yet I could not open my eyes. I seemed to go to sleep ; but after a while I felt that I was lying down, and I wondered how I could be lying down in that hole where there was not room. And next I realized that I was lying on the ground. Surely I was out of that hole. I drew a breath.

"Editha!" said a voice close to my ear; and I made a great effort, and opened my eyes.

Gaspar was bending beside me, kneeling, and the tears were running down his white face.

"You are alive," he whispered. "Alive!"

I could not speak. But Gaspar caught me up, and he and Stephen ran, carrying me. I saw that it was night still, but somehow my experience had taken all my strength from me. I could not even hold my eyes open. After being hurried for a while through the darkness, I felt that we neared the sand dunes of Scheveningen. Gaspar and Stephen seemed to be striding through sand, and the odor of the sea struck my nostrils. Swiftly we rushed on across the dunes, and by the time we reached Scheveningen, I could open my eyes. We ran through the narrow black lanes, and I turned my head on Gaspar's shoulder, and saw, dark against the sky of night, the pointed spire of the church of Scheveningen. I, who had thought never to look up at the sky again, saw the church spire and knew we were almost home. From something Stephen said, I concluded that he had gagged and bound the soldier who had been burying me.

"I would I had killed him!" muttered Stephen, savagely.

But Gaspar sternly rebuked him, saying:

"We Anabaptists do not count it Christ-like to kill men, even our enemies, and did I think it would save his life I would go back and help that soldier now."

But Stephen hastily assured Gaspar that certainly the soldier had received no injury that could result in death, and Gaspar ran with me into our house, and gave me to Thyra's care. For some days afterward I lay almost unable to move, but they were days wherein we all came to an agreement that we dared not stay longer in our present home. Not even for the sake of trying further to discover the fate of my father and mother, and Gaspar thought we would all better go to England.

CHAPTER XIII

CAPTURED

IMMEDIATELY after this agreement, however, I was taken with a long attack of fever, brought on by my fright and exhaustion during the night of my burial. I was ill for several months, and during that time we were hidden in another house, for we feared lest soldiers from the Hague should track me to our house in Scheveningen. The two other women, who were taken prisoners at the time when I was, had not been dwellers in Scheveningen, but in the Hague itself, and we had not been able to discover what was done with them.

1537 A.D. It was winter and a new year before I had recovered strength sufficiently to leave Scheveningen, though Gaspar and I were married a little before that by an Anabaptist minister who was under sentence of death at the stake, if he could be found. Inasmuch as my cousin Stephen dared not risk his life by becoming an Anabaptist, though he believed us to be right according to the precepts of the New Testament, he could not gain Thyra. She was firm in declaring that she would flee with Gaspar and me rather than accept the home that Stephen and his mother would gladly have given her on board their boat. Yet even I myself urged her not to decide hastily, for I knew how truly she loved Stephen, and I feared she would find being parted from him a greater trial than she anticipated. And who knew whether she would ever see him again. But she was most decided.

"I have not chosen hastily," she told me, her voice quivering. "I will not marry a man who stands a coward before the duty that he believes God's word commands him to perform. Editha, these are times when death is better than life, if life must be purchased by cowardice. If Stephen loves his life better than he does the Lord, he is no fit man for me."

Gaspar intended that he and Thyra and I should go to England, but, being almost discovered and captured in the attempt, we fled in terror to the shores of the Zuyder Zee. Our next three years were spent in fleeing from one place to another; sometimes in winter skating, under cover of the fog, from the pursuit of the enemies of the Anabaptists. Sometimes we stayed in one place as long as six months, and then a new danger would confront us, and we would fly again. So three years passed—three years in which Anabaptists prayed to God for the coming of religious freedom.

It was on the day our little boy, Hendrick, was one year old that we heard of the arrival in the Low Countries of the emperor, 1540 A.D.

Charles V. The coming of the emperor was the beginning of the renewal of the grievous persecutions against the "heretics"; but chiefly against the Anabaptists, for it was our sect which was most persecuted at this time. Several severe edicts were issued against Anabaptist persons and writings.

Always, through these three years of wandering, we had been minded to go to England, especially after we heard that, in 1536, King Henry had ordered that the English people should be allowed to have the Bible in their own tongue.

"It is wonderful; it is wonderful," I said to Gaspar. "Can it be true, or is it only wild news come across the sea?"

We did not know whether to believe it or not; it seemed so strange a thing for King Henry to do after fighting the New Testament so fiercely. But while we wondered whether we dared go to England, I one day met a woman who told me that the year before this fourteen Hollanders who had fled to England were there accused of being Anabaptists and were put to death, and ten others only saved themselves by recanting. Moreover, we heard that in the Articles of Religion set forth in England the sect of the Anabaptists was mentioned and condemned. There was certainly no religious liberty in England.

"It will not be safe for us to go there," Gaspar concluded.

So we stayed, fleeing from one place to another,

as I have said, and enduring such hardships that again we thought of going to England; but again, in 1539, we heard that an injunction had been issued there against those who held the opinions of the Anabaptists or possessed their books. And that same year too, there came fleeing from England sixteen men and fifteen women who had been banished for opposing infant baptism.

"Suppose we had gone to England and then been sent back to the Low Countries," we thought when we saw this poor company.

So we stayed; and the next year, as I have said, the emperor, Charles V., came to the Low Countries, and the persecutions that the Anabaptists had to endure grew more fierce than before.

Gaspar and Thyra, little Hendrick and I, at this time had our home and place of refuge in the lower part of an old windmill, in a somewhat lonely country spot outside of Delft, for we gradually turned in our wanderings, and came back toward the direction from which we had first started. I had wished to go toward that portion of the Low Countries again, if we ever thought we could dare do so, for I was anxious to see if in any way I could obtain word of Stephen and my aunt. We had not heard from them once in all our wanderings, and I suspected that Stephen, who had of course known that at first we had intended going to Norwich, in England, had never heard of our failing to escape thither. So, possibly, Stephen might have afterward left the Low

Countries and gone back to England himself with
his mother, thinking to find us there. I knew
that had been Stephen's intention, if we went,
and I was sure he must have lost track of us,
for he would not have been willing to give up
Thyra so easily. Perhaps he had heard how
nearly we were discovered the night of our attempt to flee to England. Perhaps he thought
that we had all been taken and killed at that
time. It was possible that he had mourned us as
dead. Whatever had been his thought, I was
glad that our flight had led us this far toward the
district in which Stephen and his mother had
been wont to follow the canals.

One afternoon, Gasper and I had been away
from the windmill, he working and I getting some
provisions from the Market at Delft. I was to
meet him at a certain spot outside the city, and
we were to go home together.

After I was past the rampart and the moat of
Delft, however, I was greatly startled. Among a
number of people who were passing, I came face
to face with him who had been one of the monks
at my old home of Caversham in England! I
shrank instantly with the fear of detection, but I
almost as immediately recollected that he could
hardly know me. I had changed and grown up
since then, and his eyes had not seemed to show
the slightest recognition as we passed each other.
It was over in an instant, but I had received such
a shock that I could feel myself tremble.

"He could not have known me!" I kept assuring myself. "In this dress, and grown older as I am, he could not have known me!"

My hands shook and I shivered. Cold chills crept over me. After I was out of sight of people, I ran. Gaspar was waiting for me at our appointed spot, and we hastened home to the windmill. Once securely shut in there behind the stout door with its bars, Thyra, Gaspar, and little Hendrick with me, I felt more safe. I knew King Henry had had spies on the continent, but no one would have any motive for tracing a poor, insignificant person like me. Not even a priest, baffled by my father's safe escape from England, would be likely to trace me here.

I told Gasper and Thyra of the English monk, and they agreed with me that there was no danger, especially as the priest had not known which way I went. And yet, so near had I come to danger, that I was haunted by the thought of it.

How had we dared come so near this pleasant city of Delft? Did I not remember hearing that the Reformation had made a stir there, and that ten years ago a painter on glass, named David Joris, who afterward turned to the Anabaptists, had obstructed a Catholic procession, and, as a punishishment, was whipped, imprisoned, and had his tongue bored. It was horrible to think of. And that had happened in Delft, the city so near us! And Joris' own mother had had her head cut off

N

in Delft, three years before! Why had I not thought more of these things?

A terror struck me, and then I resolutely tried to be brave.

"We came here because we thought it more safe than to stay where we were," I said to myself. "We are in the hands of God. There is no safe place for an Anabaptist in all the Low Countries. At least, I know of none. This windmill is as safe as any place. If our enemies discover us we cannot help it. I will leave it all in God's hand. If it is his will to take us quickly to heaven by the sword or by fire, his will be done. He has kept us alive hitherto. Our lives are his."

So I quieted myself.

"I will not talk more to Gaspar and Thyra about it," I resolved. "I am foolish to be worried. The priest did not know me."

I hushed Hendrick to sleep. Gaspar had lain down to rest early, for he was tired. He had worked hard.

Hours after the three others were asleep I lay awake listening to the rustle of the windmill overhead. I softly raised myself on my elbow, and strained my nerves to hearken. The low rustle of the windmill continued. I could hear little Hendrick's soft breathing, and I thought how dear he was to me and what a comfort. Long I leaned there listening, hardly breathing myself, listening to every sound. My elbow tiring with the strain, I lay softly down again and drew beneath the covering, for the old windmill was cold at times.

A drowsiness came upon me; I slept awhile and then awoke.

"We are safe," I thought; "no evil has befallen us."

Again I raised myself on my elbow, and leaned and listened to the windmill's sails. The world seemed peaceful. Why had I been afraid?

There was the sudden sound of a swift, awful blow on the door of the windmill. I sprang up, my heart beating swiftly. I trembled so that I could hardly stand. Blow on blow fell upon the door. The walls were of stone, but the stout door of wood. Gaspar had sprung up. A form hurried to us through the dark, and Thyra caught hold of my hand, without a word.

Blow after blow! We could hear the angry voices of men, cursing in Spanish, and high over all there came the piercing sound of an English voice: "Kill them! Kill them! Anabaptists! Heretics! Accursed of God! Kill them! Kill them!"

The voice rose into a spasm of fury. The old door was stout. The blows rained down.

"Kill them! Kill them!" shrieked the English voice, wild with rage. "Ah, that is right! The door breaks, does it not? Harder! They are there! They are there! Ah, it is not so easy to escape! We shall have them soon. Harder!"

Who should shriek in English at such a time?

Dutch or Spanish was what we were wont to hear.
I could not recognize the voice, but my heart misgave me that the monk of Caversham stood outside the door.

"Anabaptists! Heretics! Münsterites!"

Yells and shrieks assailed us. The door was
evidently giving way, stoutly barred as it had
been. There was one window in the windmill,
and thither we climbed to look out. It was on
the other side from the door. By the wavering
flame of torches, and by scanty moonlight, we saw
a number of Spanish soldiers guarding a company of prisoners. In front of them stood the
man who shrieked in English. He waved his
hands in excitement. His voice came more clearly
to my ears.

"Anabaptists! Anabaptists! Accursed! Accursed! Accursed!"

But no flash from any torch made his face clear
to me.

A sound of splintered wood. We could not see
the door, or the soldiers there.

"If I had but a rope," groaned Gaspar, "perhaps in the darkness I could let you down unseen. Oh, my Editha! my Editha! That you
should fall into the hands of yonder men!"

He sprang away from the window, and tore
some of the rough bedding into strips. Soon he
was beside me, knotting the strips together. His
breath came hurriedly, and he and I tugged at the
knots to see if they were strong enough.

"Now!" he whispered. "Now!"

There was a wild outcry of triumph below.

"Quick!" whispered Gaspar.

He had tied the rope around me. Thyra handed up the baby, wrapped in his covering, and still sleeping.

"Kill them! Kill them!" shrieked that English voice of madness.

Gaspar tried to help me out of the window. The ground seemed so far below. I wondered if the rope was strong enough. Gaspar let me down swiftly and carefully. I was half-way down. I could hear the shouts and the blows on the other side of the windmill. I was two-thirds down.

"Anabaptists! Anabaptists! Münsterites!"

My feet were on the ground. With despairing fingers I pulled at the knot where Gaspar had fastened me to the rope. Would it never come undone? Would those people see me?

I slipped out of the rope at last. It passed upward out of sight, and I crouched close to the windmill's side, and held my baby to my heart.

The staunch old door! If it could but hold out a little longer. The sound of splintered wood again. Thyra came flying down beside me. She loosed herself from the rope, and we waited.

There was a crash. A succession of crashes. The sound of wood that broke and fell, the shout of men who rushed inside the windmill, the partial vision of a man who shot down the rope and dropped beside me. It was Gaspar.

"Keep on this side of the windmill," he whispered.

He snatched baby Hendrick, and we ran.

Inside the windmill there were shouts and yells.

"Kill them!   Kill them!   Kill them!"
screamed the English voice.

Hendrick began to cry, disturbed in his sleep.

Gaspar hushed the child, and we ran.   Oh, we
were going to escape!   After all, the English
monk would be baffled.   Nobody would be found
in the old windmill.   We were to escape with our
lives and our New Testaments.   For, night and
day I always carried mine with me, and I was
sure that Gaspar and Thyra had theirs.   I would
not have wished to lose my English Testament,
though now I could read Dutch easily.

Alas!   What was that outcry behind us?

"There they go!   There they go!" came the
scream of the English monk.   "There! There!"

He was after us, himself and six of the soldiers.

"Come this way," panted Gaspar, and Thyra
and I ran in the direction he went.   Hendrick,
thoroughly aroused, began to cry loudly, notwithstanding all Gaspar's efforts.   The child cried
for me, and I was forced to take him, lest his
outcries should surely discover us to our pursuers.

We fled on.   The soldiers gained upon us.
The English priest was left far behind.   Oh,
could we run no faster?   Here they came!
Nearer!   Nearer!   I was so exhausted that I

almost fell. Gaspar half carried me as we sped on. The soldiers were upon us.

We were taken. Driven headlong with blows, we were hurried back to the windmill. The English monk and the soldiery greeted us with shouts of derision, and we were added to the number of other prisoners inside the guarding band. There were about thirty of our fellow-prisoners, men, women, and children, and I judged from the English monk's remarks that we were all Anabaptists.

The soldiery formed a ring about us, and began to discuss what would better be done. Should the prisoners be immediately butchered, or should we be reserved for some other doom? There was a long wrangle.

"Was not your father he who hid in a fagot pile in Caversham in England?" savagely inquired the English monk, turning to me.

He knew me then! I was silent.

"She is Dutch," interposed a Spanish soldier. "All Dutch do not talk English."

"She is English," affirmed the monk, with a fierce frown.

But the voice of the leader of the soldiery rang out commanding the prisoners to march.

We rose. My baby Hendrick kept his arms around my neck.

"Let me carry him," whispered Gaspar.

But the baby clung to me.

"Go on, Anabaptists," scornfully cried a soldier, aiming a blow at Gaspar. "Go on! We will take you to a place where you shall fare worse than in a windmill."

"That may well be," answered Gaspar calmly. "But know you, that the religious freedom which the Anabaptists ask will come some day to all the Low Countries despite the Emperor Charles, great as he is. It will come, for it is God's decree. Beware, lest you be found to fight against God."

The Spanish soldier perhaps not understanding all that my husband said, for Gaspar had spoken in Dutch, merely made the sign of the cross, and muttered an imprecation against heretics, but another of our captors, evidently understanding more perfectly, shrieked, "Freedom! We will teach you what freedom means."

And Gaspar was silent, knowing that to say anything was useless. But an Anabaptist woman beside me murmured in my ear as we were driven on : "Your husband speaks truly. There will be religious freedom some day, whether we live to see it or not. God hears the prayers of the Anabaptists."

Gaspar managed to reach my side once more. The baby had grown very heavy.

"Let me carry him," again whispered Gaspar.

But Hendrick clung to me. Oh, my baby, my baby! To think it was the last time your arms clasped my neck !

The soldiers drove us on a long way, through the half-lit dark, mocking us with shouts, cursing us, threatening us with torture, with burning,

with beheading, with a living burial, with drowning, all in the name of the emperor.

We had stumbled on for several hours. I was
growing so weary that I could hardly carry Hendrick who kept wide awake, his bright eyes fixed
on the lights and the men, and his soft, warm
little arms clinging around my neck. I was so
tired that I wavered in my walk, but Hendrick
would not willingly go to Thyra and I dared not
force him to do so, for fear of what would happen
if he should cry. My boy! I am so thankful that
I held him those last few minutes.

We had come near a canal, when one of the
brutal soldiers sprang forward to me.

"Give me the child," he roughly commanded
in Dutch.

"No," I answered.

I shook my head, and clasped my boy tightly,
for a dreadful fear shot through me.

But the soldier's fierce hands tore the child from
me. Hendrick screamed and the soldier struck
him. I sprang to the man and snatched at my
boy, but the soldier knocked me down. His
sneering voice arose.

"See, see," he mocked. "See me play the
priest! Anabaptists, I can baptize a child. See!"

And before I could gain my feet, the soldier had
thrown Hendrick far out in the canal. There was
a cry from the child, a splash in the water.

My boy! my baby boy! He was gone. I shrieked
and plunged through the soldiers, but they caught

me and drove me back.   I saw Gaspar struggle
like a madman with the men who held him.

It was all over.   Not another cry came from
the canal.   The flickering lights showed no ripple
on the far surface of the water.

The English monk laughed.   Such a laugh!
I think devils must laugh like that.

CHAPTER XIV

IN PRISON

DO you know what it is to live in prison 1550 for ten years? Do you know how long A.D. ten years can be? Do you know what it is to see the jailer come and throw you scanty food, and jeer at you, and taunt you with your helplessness? Do you know what it is to have the executioner come at midnight and choose one of your number for torture? Do you know what that means when the one chosen is your husband? Do you know what it is to lie awake the rest of the night praying in unutterable agony to God that your husband might not recant under torture? Do you know what it is to be glad to see him brought back alive though in agony? Do you know what it is to thank God that your own child is dead, because you have seen another woman's child whipped to death?

Oh, Antwerp! Antwerp! would that we could have found refuge within you from the power of our enemies. For to you, Charles V., fearing lest, rich and powerful and splendid city that you were, you would be ruined, granted some mercy. And yet, oh, Antwerp! Antwerp! before the dreadful years of persecutions for the Anabaptists were

over, how many, many hundreds of the poor martyrs were to perish in your city.   And still, at one
time, just before our escape, we had wished that
we could have been in Antwerp.

I will pass over those prison years.   Condemned
to perpetual confinement, several of our company
died before the first year had passed.   The second
year six of us died ; the third year five more.
Once in a while we heard through some new prisoner how it fared with our Anabaptist brethren
in the outer world.

And sad things we heard.   One prisoner who
came to us in the fifth year of our imprisonment,
told us that at Rotterdam, the year before, a company of Anabaptists had been holding a meeting in
a house when a woman came to the house pro-
fessedly to borrow a kettle.   She had this only as
an excuse, however, for she was a spy, and she betrayed the Anabaptist company into the hands of
the enemy.   Fine business it was for a woman to
be in.   The poor Anabaptists were tortured and
would not recant.   So the men were beheaded by
the sword, and the women were put into a boat,
and, it being cold enough so that the water was
frozen over, the boat was thrust under the ice till
the women were drowned.

I questioned Gaspar.   "Does it look as if the
Anabaptists in spite of their wishing for religious
freedom for all men, will ever gain it ? What are
we doing toward bringing religious freedom to
the world ? "

And Gaspar always uncomplaining, answered patiently: "Wait, Editha. The emperor is sworn to uphold the pope and the church of Rome. But God rules above the emperor. I will tell you what the Anabaptists are doing toward bringing religious freedom—they are praying. They are praying that that day of freedom may come. Sometimes when I lie awake I seem to see their prayers mingling with the smoke of burning martyrs in a great cloud going up from this country to God. Ours go up from the prison cells, and mingle with the prayers of those Anabaptists whose bodies lie drowned in river, or stand where they were buried alive. Wait, Editha, the Anabaptists are praying for religious freedom. Is prayer nothing? They are dying for religious freedom. Is martyrdom nothing?" An old man one of our fellow-prisoners, repeated: "The Anabaptists are praying for freedom!"

From another new prisoner who came to us one year we heard of the drowning of two Anabaptist women in sacks. Moreover we heard that throughout Flanders there had been great persecution, and that Charles V. had demanded that the Anabaptists should be expelled from Friesland. And in 1549, we heard that there were in prison at Amsterdam about twenty Anabaptists who had been put there on account of their religion. Twelve of these prisoners, through some kind friends, escaped. A tailor, named Ellert Jansen, might also have escaped, but he was lame, and

thought he would easily be retaken, so he stayed
with the others in prison, and they were all burnt
to death in March, five men and three women,
according to their sentence: "For that they had
suffered themselves to be re-baptized, and had
wrong notions of the sacraments." But, as Ellert
Jansen was being led to his death he cried out:
"This is the most joyful day in my whole life!"

1551   We prisoners sometimes felt as if death
A.D.   were preferable to imprisonment for life.
But when a little more than ten years had gone
by, after the year 1551 had come, before the ice
had left the canals, one very foggy night a daughter of a jailer, who had secretly made friends of
Thyra and me, contrived that Gaspar and we
should escape. With fear and trembling she let
us out, giving us skates and bidding us under
cover of the fog to flee away as swiftly as possible.
The girl had furnished us with food and a little
money, and noiselessly we vanished in the darkness.

I could hardly skate, we had been so long imprisoned. I thought, as we shot on, of those
skaters and those boats of Scheveningen that used
to fly past the old *treckschuyt*, when my father
and mother and I lived there. But those days
were gone. Nothing but intolerance seemed to
remain for the Low Countries. And yet, oh how
we Anabaptists had prayed that religious freedom
might come!

On we fled, side by side. The fog closed around

In Editha's Days

Skating for Liberty

Page 207

us and hid us from any other persons who might be abroad at night. We listened fearfully for any outcry behind us, but all was still. We skated through all the hours of the night, pausing to rest now and then, taking a little to eat, then skating on through the fog, not knowing whither we went, save that we would leave our prison far enough away; and we were sure, as long as we kept to the canals, that we would not lose our direction, and wander around in a circle back again to the enemies we had left, whatever new ones might appear.

Faintly through the fog in one place there loomed up before us the outline of a *treckschuyt* hemmed in by the ice. Living persons were near us. It was almost morning. We were affrighted, and yet we did not know where we were going. We were so weary, Thyra and I, that we could hardly go farther, for this was unwonted exercise for us after our prison life.

As we stood resting a moment, hidden by the fog we hoped from all observing eyes, we heard a man's voice singing. Two or three other voices joined him. It was a Dutch version of one of the Psalms, I thought. The singing was very soft indeed, so faint that if we had not been so near the *treckschuyt* we could not have heard it.

"They are at morning prayers," whispered Thyra.

At least we suspected the people on board the *treckschuyt* were not Catholics. But, if Protest-

ants, they might be our enemies. Anabaptists
must not be sure of friends.

Thyra, haggard with sleeplessness from anxiety,
looked at me. I saw the exhaustion in her face.

"The fog will lift, perhaps, when the sun rises,"
I said to Gaspar, "and we shall be left to hide as
we can. Shall we not go to this *treckschuyt?*"

If we had not been in such desperate straits we
would have hesitated more, but we were all too
exhausted to go farther.

We approached the *treckschuyt.* Gaspar climbed
on board, warning us to fly immediately if we
heard any tumult or outcry. But it was not more
than a moment before he was back again with
two other men.

"Editha," he whispered, "the Lord has led us
to Anabaptist friends. And oh, Editha, Menno
Simons is on board this *treckschuyt.*"

Oh, such a thrill of gladness as filled my heart
at that news! For Menno Simons was the com-
forter of the Anabaptists in those dark days. How
he traveled, pursued by danger, speaking to the
Anabaptists, comforting, strengthening them! He
it was whom God raised up for our aid, else had
some of us almost dwelt in darkness.

We were hurried into one of the compartments
of the *treckschuyt,* and there we found the little
company assembled. All greeted us with great
affection, and we were warmed, and fed, and comforted by sympathy. Ah! sympathy is so dear
when one has been in prison ten years.

"Unto you it has been given to suffer for our Lord's sake," said Menno Simons, "Blessed be the Lord that he gives us such grace."

Menno Simons had known what it is to be a worldly, dark-minded priest of the Romish church, yet not without some tenderness and piety. But, in 1530, he had been led to search the New Testament in order to find out the truth about the Lord's Supper. Afterward he was led, by the killing of that poor Anabaptist tailor, Sicke Snijder, to examine the New Testament in regard to baptism. You remember that the Anabaptist, Sicke Snijder, was executed with the sword, his body laid on a wheel, and his head set on a stake in Friesland, a short time after we came to the Low Countries.

Menno Simons was priest at his native place, Witmarsum, in Friesland, from 1531 to 1536, but during several of those years, he was trying to suppress his convictions that the Anabaptists were right. He knew that if he left the church of Rome and became an Anabaptist he would receive hatred and suffering. But one thing is especially noteworthy in his case, as showing how surely a frank study of the New Testament will lead to belief in immersion after repentance and faith in Christ, and will also lead to the rejection of infant baptism. Menno Simons never spoke to any Anabaptist persons about baptism till after he had become sure himself from reading the New Testament that they were right.

Menno Simons himself told Gaspar and me of his struggle before he came out from the Romish church.

"I besought my God with sighing and tears," said he, "that to me, a troubled sinner, he would grant the gift of his grace; that he would endue me with wisdom, spirit, frankness, and manly fortitude, so that I might preach his worthy name and holy word unadulterated, and proclaim his truth to his praise.

"At length the great and gracious Lord, perhaps after the course of nine months, extended to me his fatherly spirit, help, and mighty hand, so that I freely abandoned at once my character, honor, and fame which I had among men, also my anti-Christian abominations, mass, infant baptism, loose and careless life, and all, and put myself willingly in all trouble and poverty under the pressing cross of Christ my Lord."

Menno Simons told Gaspar moreover: "By the gracious favor of God I have acquired my knowledge, as well of baptism as of the Lord's Supper, through the enlightening of the Holy Spirit, attendant on my much reading and contemplating the Scripture, and not through the efforts and means of seducing sects, as I am accused."

It was the 12th of January, 1536, the year before Gaspar and Thyra and I fled from Scheveningen, that Menno Simons bravely resigned and left the Roman Catholic church. He began to preach secretly to those brethren who came around him. But the Inquisition had its eyes on Menno Simons. He did not preach so secretly that the Inquisition could not discover what he was doing.

But he was such a comfort to God's people. He traveled hither and thither, always persecuted, always in danger, but preaching and bringing many to the truth. It was well that he came to comfort the Low Country Anabaptists when he did, for to how many scattered and oppressed communities did his eloquent words and powerful religious writings prove a blessing! He held up our faith. He had left ease and plenty for flight and suffering. He was our brother in tribulation, and his words brought us good cheer.

On this *treckchuyt*, he and his wife, as well as we, were refugees. After we had been made comfortable, and after Thyra, who was nearly exhausted, had lain down in the other compartment to sleep, Gaspar and I tried to learn from the other Anabaptists in hiding all we could of what had gone on in the world since we were imprisoned. For you cannot think what it is to be shut off from the world and have it go on so long without you, and then come out into it again.

"We want to flee to Norwich in England, if we can escape the Inquisition," Gaspar said. "How does King Henry treat those who are not Roman Catholics? Does he allow people to read the Bible now? We heard a rumor once that he did."

There was a solemn silence in the little company. One person looked at another.

"You see," commented one old man, "what it is to be in prison so long."

"King Henry?" repeated the old man, turning to Gaspar. "It makes no difference now in England whether King Henry likes the Bible or not. Four years ago King Henry went to stand before God."

Gaspar and I both started.

"Is King Henry dead?" I asked.

The little company assured us it was so.

"And who reigns now?" we inquired, breathlessly.

"A young king, Edward," answered the old man. "He is but fourteen years old. Heaven grant he become a better man than was his father. Yes; he allows the people to read the Bible."

Gaspar and I looked at one another.

"We will go to England," we declared. "We will go to England."

"If the Inquisition does not seize you before escaping from the Low Countries," warned one sad-faced woman. "We all intend to flee to England, but so many of us are taken before arriving there. And even there an Anabaptist has not much home."

Now all these years had I cherished a hope in my heart that my Cousin Stephen and my aunt had gone back to England at the time we tried to flee thither, and it seemed to me that it would be so great and wonderful a joy to find them again, though I could not hope that Stephen had waited

all these years for Thyra, whom he must regard
as dead. Probably he had married, after the manner of men. Yet a wonderful joy thrilled through
me at the mere thought of seeing one of my own
kin again.

But at the words of this woman my joy was
tinged with anxiety. The Inquisition did hold
sway. Was it at all probable that we could escape
from this country?

We fell to discussing what the Inquisition had
already done. We knew the *treckschuyt* might be
invaded, and we might all be arrested at any
moment. Menno Simons told us of two excellent
men named Eelken and Fye, Anabaptists of the
town of Olde Boor, in West Friesland. These
men, two years before this, had been apprehended
and brought to the magistrates. Sentence was
pronounced. Eelken was beheaded. Fye was to
be burned. The constable said: "I have in my
life seen many a heretic, but never a more obstinate one than this." Fye was strangled and then
burnt, but the common people cried out: "That
was a pious man. If he was not a Christian there
is not one in the whole world."

Moreover, Menno Simons told us of a good
Anabaptist, Hans of Overdam, who had been put
to death at Ghent with Hans Keeskooper during
the last year. The council had asked the prisoners why they were not satisfied with the faith of
their parents and with their baptism. Their reply
was: "We know of no infant baptism; but of a

baptism upon faith, which God's word teacheth
us." There was much discussion, and a monk became so angry that he cried out, "Simpletons!
Simpletons! Heretics! Ye are heretics!" Hans
of Overdam, before his martyrdom, wrote a letter
giving an account of his imprisonment, saying in
one place: "Eleven of us were taken into a dark,
deep vault. In the vault were built many dark
cells of masonry. There we were all put, three
and three; but Hansken and I were placed in the
darkest of all, in which was a little dirty straw, as
much as might be carried in one's lap." When
the prisoners had been on the way to the castle
whither they were first taken, Hans and his fellow-
prisoner had been fastened together with iron
bands, their thumbs being also fastened together.
This letter, which Hans of Overdam requested
should be forwarded to Friesland, wishing that
his words might reach the church at Embden,
contained also these words: "Written in prison
for the testimony of Christ. In this dark dungeon
I have lain a month. I now lie in a deep, round
dungeon, which is somewhat lighter, and in which
I have written this letter." So afterward did this
good man and his friend die at the stake.

"And while such things go on," indignantly
added one of the men hiding with us on board
the *treckschuyt*, "the Emperor Charles has ordered
the inquisitors 'to make it known that they are
not doing their own work, but that of Christ, and
to persuade all persons of the fact.' It would

be hard work to persuade me of that, I can tell
you."

"If the Lord Christ himself should appear in
human form in this country, who can doubt that
he would be seized and crucified again or burned
alive by the order of the emperor?" asked one of
the woman, adding: "The emperor puts to death
those who try to follow Christ most closely."

"Be of good cheer," gently answered Menno
Simons ; "the God of religious freedom yet reigns.
Let us pray to him to deliver all men from tyr-
anny."

And then he prayed. Such a prayer! Full of
pity for our persecutors who thought, some of
them, that they did God service ; full of sympathy
for the sufferings of our fellow-brethren ; a petition that God would send religious freedom to all
men. One after another of the company prayed.
Always that request ran through the prayers, that
God would send religious freedom. Freedom!
Freedom to read God's word, and to obey it.
Freedom not for us only, but for all men.

And yet our little prayer meeting would have
been considered a heinous thing, had the Emperor
Charles known of it. Had he not forbidden all
reading of the Scriptures, all discussion within
one's own house of religious matters? He would
no more tolerate freedom than, a few years after
this, would Viglius van Aytta van Zuichem, he
who was a member of the State council under
Margaret, and president of the council of Mechlin.

"If every man," said Viglius, "is to believe what he likes in his own house, we shall have hearth gods and tutelar divinities again, the country will swarm with a thousand errors and sects, and very few there will be, I fear, who will allow themselves to be enclosed in the sheepfold of Christ. I have ever considered this opinion the most pernicious of all. They who hold it have a contempt for all religion, and are neither more nor less than atheists. This vague, fireside liberty should be by every possible means extirpated ; therefore did Christ institute shepherds to drive his wandering sheep back into the fold of the true church ; thus only can we guard the lambs against the ravening wolves and prevent their being carried away from the flock of Christ to the flock of Belial. Liberty of religion or of conscience, as they call it, ought never to be tolerated."

Yet it was this "fireside liberty" for all men for which we Anabaptists worked and prayed. We would give up our lives before we would give up our right to freedom of conscience.

Several of our little company of Anabaptists purposed trying to reach Antwerp, where the Inquisition had less power. The night following our coming to the *treckschuyt* was foggy also, and several of our new Anabaptist friends bade us farewell and started for Antwerp. Alas! if they reached that city I know not whether they found safety there, for it was in September of this same year that two Anabaptists, we heard, were mar-

tyred at the stake at Antwerp ; and the wife of one
was taken to the river Scheldt, put into a sack and
drowned. So Anabaptists were not safe in Antwerp,
though the Inquisition did not rage there as elsewhere.

We stayed on board the *treckschuyt* yet
another day ; and then the next night, accompanied by the prayers of our new friends, Gaspar
and Thyra and I set out on our journey to the
coast to see if we might find any means of leaving
the Low Countries for England. In our skating
before, we had unwittingly been going away from
the coast, instead of toward it.

In spite of all that I knew was against our undertaking, I could not help feeling glad, and pic-
turing to myself our joyfully reaching Norwich
and our finding my relatives there. It was only
a vision of what might never be, and yet it put
new strength into me as I skated on, my old New
Testament hidden about me. For, through the
years of confinement, I had contrived to conceal
my New Testament and keep it, although Gaspar's Dutch Testament had been speedily discovered and taken from him, and Thyra's had been
found, after a time, and taken from her.

By dint of much hiding and traveling by night,
we at length reached the seacoast. Ah, that
North Sea with its gray sky and continual uproar !
How many memories came back to me, as I
looked out on the water again !

"We are on the edge of freedom," I thought,

and I remembered how among the yellow dunes beside the farther stretches of this sea, Gaspar years ago had asked me to be his wife and had asked me to go with him to England. If we had gone then, would it have been better with us now? At least, my baby's curly head would never have sunk beneath the waters of a canal of the Low Countries.

There were dunes all along the coast, and Gaspar thought that we might find more safety traveling and living among the sand dunes than elsewhere. It was one day when we were hidden among these dunes that we saw a thing dreadful to view.

It was afternoon. The breeze from the water was in our faces. Thyra slept. Gasper and I watched, lest an enemy should surprise us. Gaspar came sliding down from the top of a sand dune.

"There approach men across the dunes!" he warned, and I hastily woke Thyra.

Before long we heard voices, as the company of men passed by our range of sand dunes. A woman's voice in Dutch, repeated the words of John 3 : 16 :

" *Want alzoo lief heeft God de wereld gehad, dat Hij zijnen eeniggeboren Zoon gegeven heeft, opdat een iegelijk, die in Hem gelooft, niet verderve, maar het eeuwige leven hebbe.*"

And a man's voice, loud and terrible, replied : "Anabaptist, what know you of the Scriptures?

Have you then read them? So much the more ought you to die! Anabaptist! Heretic!"

They passed on, and, afraid as we were of discovery, we could not forbear creeping up a sand dune's top, and watching what came to pass. The men took the girl,—for she was only a young girl who was thus doomed,—to the edge of the sea where the surf came rushing in with great and angry force. We could not hear what was said, but we feared for the young Anabaptist. She seemed to have no friends with her in this her hour of need, and she knew nothing of our sympathizing eyes.

"Oh!" cried Thyra, clasping her hands in horror.

The men had driven the girl into the sea. One of the soldiers dealt her a most savage blow on the head, and she fell forward into the foaming water. Horror-stricken, we watched the body float out, sometimes visible, sometimes obscured by the dashing waves. She lay on her back, and floated.

"She must be dead," whispered Gaspar, after we had watched some time. "If she had been breathing she would have choked with water and have sunk before now. But she floats! I think that blow from the soldier must have killed her."

The soldiers who had finished their work with certainty, as they apparently thought, went away through the sand dunes. We watched the men disappear and reappear between the ranges. The soldiers were gone at last. The body of the girl still floated.

We hurried down on the sands as near as we dared. Gaspar looked at the surf.

"I must see if she is dead! Possibly she may be alive even yet," he said; and cold winter day as it was, pulled off his outer garments and plunged into the surf.

He swam toward the body, battling with the waves that threatened to overwhelm him. But, though he swam as a wonted fisherman, yet the strength of the surf was such that he could not come near enough to the girl to grasp her. He would swim almost to her, and then the waves would bear him away again. Once he was so near that he thought the next wave would bring her to him, but instead of that the wave floated her farther away.

By this time he was quite sure she was dead; yet, if he could have brought her body to shore he would have done so, in order that we might give her decent burial in the sands. But he was compelled to give up at last and swim for the shore, feeling that his strength was failing in that sea. Thyra and I, who had been greatly alarmed for him, watched him striving through the waves. We ran down to their edge and pulled him in. He was almost exhausted, but we did all we could for him. After he was half buried in the sand on the side of a dune away from the wind, we turned our attention again to the drowned girl.

For about two hours Thyra and I watched the body of the girl floating, floating, always on her back. At last the waves brought her to a place where there seemed to be a kind of an eddy in the water. We lost sight of her an instant, and then she reappeared, but the eddy had turned her over, so that she lay upon her face a moment. And then she began slowly to disappear.

"Oh, she is going down!" exclaimed Thyra.

Little by little the girl sank, till finally her long hair spread out upon the water, and that was the last we saw of her as she went down.

Thyra drew a great breath. We watched a few moments, but the murdered girl did not reappear on the water.

"She is gone!" I whispered.

In the wind and the rain of the following night we traveled as far as possible among the dunes. And when next day I slept, hidden in the sand, I dreamed I saw the body of that young Christian girl floating upon the waves.

CHAPTER XV

ESCAPE TO ENGLAND

TRAVELING along the coast as swiftly as possible, we at length reached the vicinity of Scheveningen. Out on the sand dunes, a night's walk from the village, we were startled and made horribly afraid by finding a long pole, and hanging from the top, a dead man, swaying a little in the wind. His head hung heavily drooping forward ; one arm swung helplessly. He was bound to the pole with ropes. His was a ghastly figure ; some long, torn portion of his raiment was swinging down from his shoulder ; ropes were about his neck and his drooping shoulders, his knees, and one ankle. One hand was tied to his side, the other arm as I said was swaying, and his head, as far as we could judge in the uncertain light, had been partly crushed by a heavy stone or instrument. His ghastly form seemed almost to come to life before our eyes; the effect doubtless of the moving arm and swaying portion of his attire.

He had evidently been dead for days, although at first thinking him alive from his motion, we had spoken to him. But we spoke to the dead. We hurried past, feeling that the sand dunes were well known to our enemies. We could not doubt that he who hung there had been slain on account of his religion. I looked back fearfully, and saw him swaying, a dark, startling form, fading out against the gray sky.

"If we hasten we may reach Scheveningen before day," said Gaspar.

"Will any one remember us?" asked Thyra. "Will any one take us in?"

Nevertheless, when we saw the fishing boats of Scheveningen drawn up on the beach as of old, and when we saw the church-spire dark above the dunes, we cried out for joy, and ran over the sands. We reached the city at last, though it seemed as if sand dune after sand dune would intervene. We hastened up a narrow lane and hid ourselves. Finally we ventured to a house that we had once known. Despite the years of prison-life, the fisher-woman knew us, and took us in immediately.

And here, for the first, I heard news of Stephen. The woman remembered him and his mother, and assured us that they had without doubt gone to England soon after the time of our flight.

"And you, have you been there and been banished?" she asked.

We told her the story of our wanderings, and she was pitiful, but doubted whether we three could leave the Low Countries unperceived.

"The eyes of the Inquisitors and of your enemies are quick to see," she whispered.

"Their eyes may be holden that they may not know us," answered Gaspar, undismayed.

And so did he encourage me by his words, that I said to Thyra when we were alone together, " I think we shall see England and Stephen before long."

But Thyra only threw herself into my arms, and wept as if she would never be done. And I could not comfort her, knowing right well that Stephen must count her as dead, and if he had wedded another, it was but human and manlike that he should have done so. Moreover, she had definitely refused him, because he would not dare to follow his highest convictions. Yet I, who am a woman and know a woman's heart, pitied my sister Thyra, notwithstanding she said never a word why she wept.

But though we tried continually to find passage 1551 to England, so fearful were we of discovery A.D. by our enemies, it was not till September that we effected our escape.

It was a gray, dark September night when we and a man, who also said that he wished to go to England, went out of Scheveningen. We had much hope that a vessel of which we had heard would bear us to the land we sought. The vessel was to lie by for us at a certain point, which we were to reach in a small boat.

We had come to the outermost edge of the dunes in safety, when out of the night and the sands four men appeared and pursued us. We succeeded in escaping them in the darkness, but we were so driven out of our course that we hardly knew what to do. The man who was with us, named Johannes, had professed to us that he was an Anabaptist also. But I began to doubt him, for while we fled from our pursuers, I thought I had heard him call back something that seemed as if he were in league with them. Yet he had continued running with us, and now stood beside us thanking God that we had escaped. I knew not what to think.

After a time we ventured back to the place where our small boat had been secreted. Finding no one to oppose us, we entered the boat and pushed off, hidden by the darkness.

When we had rowed a distance, the man Johannes suddenly sprang to his feet, struck Gaspar a violent blow with an oar, and attempted to throw him overboard. The men grappled fiercely in the darkness. The waves were tossing the boat, and swayed by the struggles of the men, it careened from one side to the other, till it seemed as though it would capsize. Thyra and I grasped Johannes, trying to keep him from dealing Gaspar such blows, but we were little against the hypocrite's strength. He was furious, having evidently thought his power sufficient to overcome Gaspar without difficulty. But my husband, despite his prison experiences, still retained much of the strength with which he had formerly faced the North Sea.

Johannes dealt Gaspar a mighty blow, and half pushed him overboard. Another instant, and the hypocrite's purpose would be achieved. But Gaspar, recovering himself, smote Johannes, and immediately the boat capsized, and we were all thrown into the sea.

There was an awful interval of struggling to catch hold of the boat. I grasped it, and looked around. The night and the waves hid all. I heard a voice beside me, Gaspar's voice, though what he said the waves dashed from me.

"Thyra!" I screamed, striving to pierce the dark with my eyes.

Had she gone down? And where was Johannes the traitor?

"Gaspar!" cried a faint voice through the wash of waves.

We shouted back.

"I am safe!" cried Thyra. "I have caught an oar. I can swim."

She came closer.

But where was Johannes?

We called aloud, but the waves only answered us. We clung to the boat and drifted, calling till we felt we must not lose our strength shouting. Johannes had returned no cry. Yet I felt as if any instant he might seize and try to drown me.

We floated and swam, holding the boat till after being in the water for more than an hour, we succeeded in reaching the shore quite a distance beyond Scheveningen. Here we righted the boat, and drew it on the sands. All our provisions and little possessions had sunk when the boat was overturned. Everything we had provided was gone. We lay on the sands exhausted. Already midnight must be past. The vessel on which we were to sail was to wait for us, if necessary till near morning, but no longer.

Gaspar sat up.

"I must return to Scheveningen and find help," he murmured. "I am too weak to row to the ship."

With that he fell back on the sand and answered no more, though I spoke to him. In alarm, Thyra and I tried to lift him, but his head hung back helplessly. His heart beat still. Oh, how I longed for light that I might see his face! If, when he was in the water, he had swooned like this, what should we have done?

I could not comprehend why he did not revive now. But daylight came faintly at last, and then Thyra and I cried out, for it was blood as well as water, that made his left sleeve wet. Pulling bare his arm, I found a knife-cut, not deep indeed, but bleeding yet.

"That traitor, Johannes, had a knife," groaned Thyra, as we bound the arm.

After a while Gaspar revived enough to tell us that we must reach Scheveningen before morning. He tried to walk, though he was still so weak that we supported him as well as we could. We were obliged to stop often for rest, but continued, till by the time morning fully came, we had reached Scheveningen and found shelter with our kind friend.

Now whether Johannes, the traitor, struck on his own knife when the boat capsized, or whether he went down among those waves, I cannot tell, but I know that, during our stay of ten days after this in Scheveningen, that man who had pretended to be an Anabaptist was never seen. After ten days we went forth again, two of the Scheveningen fishermen being with us, and lying in the bottom of the fishing-boat, concealed by an old sail, we were brought by our friends to a ship that was to bear us to England.

But I have never doubted that Johannes was one of those informers whom Charles V., in his edict of 1550, encouraged to betray heretics into the hands of the inquisitors. It is true we had almost no goods, with the possession of which Johannes might have been rewarded for his treachery; but perhaps he looked for reward elsewhere if he could but take us prisoners. It was doubtless his intention also to reveal to our enemies the name of the kind friend who sheltered us in Scheveningen. The edict had forbidden any one to lodge a heretic, or furnish him with food, fire, or clothing. But I have little doubt that the waves of the North Sea covered both Johannes and his evil purposes.

Tossing in our ship, we thanked God for his protection in the past. It seemed wonderful that we were really out of the Low Countries at last; and even in the waves of this sea there was a feeling of security. The God who had kept us

through so many perils owned this ocean, held us
and it in the hollow of his hand, and could bring
us unto our desired haven, no matter what the
will of our enemies might be.

One day my husband came to me with beaming
face.

"Editha," he said, eagerly. " I have a Dutch
Testament again."

In the ship on which we were, we had found
numerous fleeing Anabaptists. It was from
one of these men that Gaspar had obtained
his Testament; and I was very thankful he could
do so, for English Testaments might be more
numerous in England than Dutch ones, and there
is nothing like one's own home tongue. Incred-
ible as it might seem, considering the experiences
through which we had passed, I still had my old,
worn English Testament, though surely I would
have lost it before this had I not always made a
practice of carrying the book concealed inside my
dress. Stained with sea-water and faded with
much reading, that New Testament was dearer to
me than any newer copy that England might
hold, for my old book seemed the only link left
to bind me to the days when my father and my
mother were alive.

But oh, when the shores of England came in
sight, what a weeping arose among us all ! Many
wept for joy, crying out that the land of religious
freedom was before us. One Anabaptist, a cripple
through the tortures inflicted and whose wife had

been buried alive in the land we left, sobbed aloud
and blessed the young boy, King Edward, who
allowed his subjects to read the word.   But Anabaptists might perhaps not be welcome for all that.
Most of us were bound for Norwich, which
another King Edward had once made the home
of many persons from the Low Countries, and
where we were to hear that England was not such
a land of religious freedom after all.

Yet England, to many of those who wept, did
not mean what it did to me.   It was my homeland.   And were Stephen and my aunt still in
Norwich? That had not been a place without
its martyrdom for conscience' sake, and Gaspar
and I talked of Thomas Bilney who years before
this had, after recanting and suffering greatly in
spirit because of that recantation, obtained grace
of God and coming to Norwich preached in the
fields, confessing his past weakness and warning
all men "to beware by him, and never to trust to
their fleshly friends in matters of religion."   He
gave one of Tyndale's New Testaments to a converted nun, was arrested, put into prison, and
afterward burned.

I thought of Thomas Bilney when at last our
weary journey ended and our company entered
into the old town of Norwich.   Would other
flames for other martyrs ever blaze in these
fields? Would Anabaptists be safe in England?
It was a solemn question to us, for we had just
heard that though Bible reading had been re-

stored, yet it must be that King Edward was against the Anabaptists, for when he had issued his general pardon in the end of December of the year before he had not included the Anabaptists. That did not look like safety or like religious toleration.

Yet Gaspar and Thyra and I found temporary shelter and set ourselves to weaving with great diligence, hoping that peace might be granted to us. We heard nothing of Stephen or my aunt.

One day Thyra came in with a face so white that on my glancing up from my weaving I asked her what the matter was. She made me but little answer, and I was busy and did not question. After a few days I began to notice that whenever we were out in the street and some of the black-robed Benedictine friars of the place went by, or whenever one such monk passed our home, Thyra would look earnestly as if she half thought to see some one. But I did not understand till one day, in a narrow, winding street, I came face to face with a thin, weary-looking Benedictine friar, whose black robe only added to his sorrowful appearance.

"Stephen! Stephen!" I cried, springing forward.

I could not but know him, though as I gazed the resemblance seemed to fade. He looked at me with hollow eyes that dropped their lids before the recognition in my face.

"I am Brother Barnabas," he murmured, drawing his black garments about him.

I could see him tremble. He stepped forward as if to pass me. I caught a fold of his black garb.

"You are Stephen, my cousin Stephen!" I asserted. "Where is my aunt? Why are you a monk?"

The slight black figure bent its head and stood quivering.

"My mother is with the dead," he replied at last. "When I returned to England I became a monk at my mother's earnest request. I am Brother Barnabas. If you are risen from the dead to break my heart with past memories, let me tell you a monk has no heart. Let me pass."

But I clung to his black robe.

"You are Stephen, Stephen my cousin," I repeated ; "Stephen who used to go with me to see the one-winged angel ; Stephen who used to listen with me to my aunt's tales of the saints ; Stephen who fled with us and who lived with us on the *treckschuyt* and learned to read the New Testament ; Stephen who believed the Anabaptists to be right and yet dared not risk his life by becoming one of that hated sect ; Stephen, whom Thyra ——"

A groan broke from the figure beside me. His face was muffled in his black robe. A monk has no heart?

"Oh, Editha, Editha!" groaned his voice. "If *she* had lived ——"

"She has," I answered sternly. "Thyra and

Gaspar and I are alive. All those persons who follow God's word and their consciences do not die, whatever men's threats may be. You might have been an Anabaptist, and yet be more alive than you seem."

I spoke plainly, for my heart was hot when I thought of his cowardice and that he had not even given me a fitting greeting after all these years of separation.

But I forgave him everything, for he fell at my feet, and broke into such sobbing that if the narrow little street had not been a somewhat unused one, we would have attracted attention. It was not "Brother Barnabas" who knelt at my feet. It was my cousin Stephen, whose sorrows I had often soothed when we were children. Yet I made no effort to comfort him now. Though he should weep long his tears could not efface the years of loneliness that Thyra had endured because of his cowardice, nor could efface the years in which, to please his mother, he had lived a life that he must have known to be a false one.

And yet, as I looked upon him sobbing there, I thought that at least the Romish church had done one thing. Stephen was a monk, and therefore unmarried. Yet what availed that now? Was it likely that this weak man had courage now to become an Anabaptist, after being bound more tightly than ever to the church of his mother's faith? And Thyra—had she seen him in this Benedictine garb?

Stephen rose to his feet.

"I am brother Barnabas," he said, brokenly. "The past is over. I am a monk. My dying mother charged me to remain one, no matter how England's religion might change."

And with a swift sign of the cross, he went away from me so quickly that I could not stay him.

I did not know whether to tell Thyra or not. But I told Gaspar, and one evening he brought Brother Barnabas home to us. By what persuasion my husband did so, I know not, neither do I know what Thyra said to Stephen, for my husband and I left them to speak to each other as they would. But this I know that, nevermore was Brother Barnabas seen to wear the garb of the Benedictine monks of Norwich.

There was a stir among the monks for a time, and we thought it advisable for Stephen to hide from them. But this was a Protestant land under King Edward's power, and men who would have burned Stephen under another ruler, now felt it wise to appear favorable themselves toward Protestantism. But Protestantism is not Anabaptism, and I feared for my cousin's life after he was baptized. For he did become an Anabaptist, great as was the danger, and I think he truly repented of the manner in which he had allowed his mother to sway his conscience. Yet I cannot deny that my cousin was a weak man, though a Christian, and I was glad the day when I saw Thyra married to him, for I trusted that her strong faith and belief would uphold him, and that he would, like many another man, be built up in the gospel by his wife's influence.

Yet, for fear of any revenge from the Benedictine friars, Stephen and his wife left us for a time, and went to Sandwich to live, thinking it more safe.

So Gaspar and I were left alone, but not for very long. God gave to us another baby boy. And when I kissed our little one, I could not keep from weeping, for I remembered his brother's curly head and the warm baby arms that had encircled my neck before the Spanish soldier snatched my darling from me. Yet my little Hendrick was in heaven, safe with my father and my mother, I believed. We named this boy Eliezer, because of the meaning of that word, "to whom God is help."

"If the child finds life such a thing as his father and mother have found it, he will have need of God's help," said Gaspar, reverently and uncomplainingly. "We will teach the little lad where real help comes from in dark days. And we will teach him also to pray with us for religious freedom."

I think I never saw a father love a child more than Gaspar loved this little English boy of ours. We hoped for peaceful days under King Edward, for we said to each other that when our young king grew older, he would see for himself that the

Anabaptists were his loyal subjects, and would treat us as kindly as the other Protestants.

1553 A.D. But when our little Eliezer was six months old, a great blow was given to our hopes, and we were thrown into a greatly unsettled state, not knowing what should befall us. Our sixteen-years-old king, Edward, died. During his reign the images had been removed from the churches, the articles known as the "Bloody Statute" had been repealed, and the Reformation progressed in England. Would such things be, under whomsoever came after him?

Lady Jane Gray, poor woman, reigned ten days. Then Mary, daughter of Henry VIII., was set on the throne, and she caused Lady Jane Gray and her husband to be beheaded. Alas, for the throne that is grasped by a bloody hand!

1553 A.D. Already we heard murmurings that our new queen was a Catholic. In August we were sure that a reaction had taken place in the government. Gardiner was made lord chancellor the 23d of August. He and that English prelate, Bonner, who afterward showed himself so great a persecutor of the Protestants, were at the head of the government.

I could see that Gaspar thought trouble at hand. Mary was not like her half-brother, Edward. Even during his reign, Anabaptists had been burned. We heard, little by little, much that showed us that Mary was a firm Papist. She had been persuaded to let King Edward's body be buried by Cranmer with the English service, but the same day had a requiem mass sung in Latin in the Tower, Gardiner wearing a mitre and performing the mass in the old popish form.

Moreover, we heard that toward the end of August Bishop Bonner restored the old service in St. Paul's church in London, there being processions of priests, and mass was also in Latin. We learned too, that there was a great revival of Catholic doings among the Oxford folk, and we heard rumors of Catholic rejoicing and plotting against the Protestants. But worse was yet to come. We lived through that winter in a state of suspense. The next summer a thing happened that crushed all hope. Queen Mary was married to that deadly foe of Anabaptists, Philip II., the son of that emperor whose dreadful power we had felt in the Low Countries, Charles V., of Spain.

"Oh, Gaspar," I cried; "the Spanish power will rule in England. We shall have the Inquisition here as it was in the Low Countries. Oh, I never thought that Spain would reach across the the sea. Woe unto us Anabaptists! We shall never see religious freedom in England."

But Gaspar, though he laid his hand on little Eliezer's head as if to keep the child from harm, answered steadily: "The Inquisition will not come to England. The English people hate the Spanish alliance too much for that."

Yet soon after Mary's marriage, persecution began more fiercely; and when November saw the declaration by Cardinal Pole that England and Rome were reconciled, and when, in February, John Rogers was burned, we prepared ourselves 1555 for the worst. I was greatly alarmed for A. D. Stephen and Thyra, from whom we had not heard for a long time. Surely now the monks would feel that they might take vengeance on the recreant Brother Barnabas.

But when I thought of John Rogers' death by fire, he being the first man to die thus under the new queen's reign, I remembered something that Rogers had said when Edward was king. A Baptist woman, named Joan Boucher, of high parentage, who had been accustomed to secretly bring copies of Tyndale's New Testament into King Henry's court was after a while taken prisoner for heresy. Those who examined her, reported to the young king that they had decreed her separation from the Lord's flock as a diseased sheep. Yet a time passed before sentence was pronounced. Ridley, and Cranmer, and Latimer, good men though they were, afterward bravely undergoing death during Queen Mary's reign, yet did not believe in allowing freedom of thought and judgment about the Scriptures. And so at last the council issued a warrant to the lord chancellor to make out a writ for Joan Boucher's execution.

Poor young King Edward did not want to give his signature to a document authorizing the killing of this woman. But Cranmer is said to have urged him to sign the document.

King Edward hesitated.

Cranmer said that by the law of Moses blasphemers were to be stoned to death; and this woman was guilty of impiety in the sight of God, impiety that a prince, as God's deputy, ought to punish.

The poor young king, evidently thinking Cranmer believed that Joan Boucher was not a Christian, asked a solemn question: "My lord, will you send her soul to hell?"

King Edward at last was compelled to yield, but he said: "If it be an error you, my lord, shall answer it to God."

So weeping, King Edward signed the document.

John Rogers too thought that Joan Boucher ought to be put to death, and when some one said that it was cruel, Rogers stated that burning alive was "no cruel death, but easy enough."

So Joan Boucher, the Baptist, was burned at the stake in May, 1550, and when in February, 1555, under Queen Mary's rule, John Rogers himself was burned at the stake, I wondered if he still thought that burning alive was "no cruel death, but easy enough."

Yet I do not doubt that Rogers, and Cranmer, and Ridley, and Latimer, were Christian men, and that they thought they did God service by burning Joan Boucher, though I think that when they met her afterward in heaven they probably believed more in religious freedom than when on

earth! It seemed that the Anabaptists were the
only people in those days who did believe in religious freedom for all men. The Catholics wished
religious freedom for themselves and the Protestants for themselves, but both denied it to the
Anabaptists. It was generally known that there
were a great many Anabaptists in the kingdom.
What would our new Queen Mary do?

What would she do, she who believed and
obeyed Rome so scrupulously that she had put
off her coronation till she had received from Gran-
vella, Bishop of Arras, the oil to be used in the
ceremony? She was afraid that, owing to the
estrangement that had existed between England
and Rome, the English oil might have lost its
virtue. But Philip, whom she married the year
after her coronation, as I have before said, had
something else to do besides introduce the Inquisition into England. In the autumn of this same
year of his marriage, his father, Charles V., resigned the crown to him, and he was left to struggle with the problem of quelling Protestantism and
stamping out all Anabaptism in the Low Countries. A goodly problem that was, but Philip
perhaps thought he could solve it.

"Better not reign at all," he was wont to say,
"than reign over heretics."

One thing puzzled us. A Spanish friar, Alfonso
de Castro, who was Philip's confessor, preached a
sermon immediately after the first martyrs were
burnt at Smithfield, England. The friar spoke

bitterly against such burnings. He denounced them as contrary to the spirit of Christianity, which is charity and forgiveness, and which teaches its ministers not to take vengeance on the sinner, but to enlighten him as to his errors, and bring him to repentance.

Now we knew not what to think, for we could hardly believe that the Spanish friar would dare speak this way without Philip's permission, and yet we did not believe, judging from the conduct of Philip's father, and from what we knew about Philip himself, that he was so very much shocked by those Smithfield burnings. The burning of heretics in England could not shock him so much more than the burning of them in Spain. And so we concluded that perhaps Philip, seeing that many people in England were shocked by the martyrdoms, thought that he would free himself from any suspicion in regard to them, and so induced his confessor to preach that sermon.

However it was, Gaspar and I, notwithstanding many alarms, stayed quietly in Norwich, for the period of Queen Mary's reign, always on the alert, always knowing that before nightfall of any day we might be imprisoned and condemned. Our queen's reign seemed drenched in blood. What would it matter to her if Gaspar and I were added to the list of victims? We were only Anabaptists.

But in spite of the cruelties of her reign, I cannot doubt that Mary was sincere in her religious

Q

professions. She was always ready to sacrifice
her own interests whenever she thought that the
interests of what she believed to be religion demanded it. She persisted in restoring the Catholic church property, which in the past had been
confiscated to the use of the crown.

Mary's ministers remonstrated.

"The crown is too impoverished to admit of
it," stated they, when they knew her plan of re-
linquishing that portion of her revenue.

"I would rather lose ten crowns," answered
Mary, "than place my soul in peril."

So does Rome deceive the heart and blind the
eyes of the one who is taught of her.

And still, through these years of blood, the
Baptists of England, miscalled Anabaptists, prayed
God to send religious liberty. It seemed at times
as if our prayers were all forgotten. And the Anabaptists of the Low Countries were praying too.
Were all our prayers to be unanswered? Ah, the
God of religious freedom was treasuring up those
prayers. In his time he would answer his suffering people.

CHAPTER XVI

DARK DAYS

"EDITHA," said Gaspar one night, "I 1558 had word from Stephen to-day." A.D.

"What said he?" I asked quickly, for my thoughts were ever with Stephen and Thyra now, knowing what peril the ex-monk and his wife might be in.

"He thinks he must flee from England," went on Gaspar. "He and Thyra are closely concealed at Sandwich, and he beseeches us to come with all speed, if we would see them again."

"Let us go," I answered hastily.

"Moreover," continued Gaspar in a low tone, "I was warned to-day that we are in danger ourselves."

"Let us go," I repeated. "Remember Richard Woodman."

"I remember he said that he praised God because he was as a sheep appointed to be slain," replied Gaspar.

"So might we rejoice, if we were taken," I responded. "But perhaps we may escape."

And we made ready that night our things, I thinking all the time how dear a place a home is, and wondering if we should ever have one again.

But I remembered him who had no place to lay his head, and was comforted.

I remembered, moreover, what the Baptist martyr, Richard Woodman, had said : "For as Christ hath given his life for us, so ought we to give our lives for the defense of the gospel and comfort of our brethren."

And lest you should not know who Richard Woodman was, I will say that he was an ironmonger of Warbleton, in Sussex, in which county he was martyred for conscience' sake.

And because Sussex is next to Kent, in the eastern part of which, at Sandwich, were Thyra and Stephen, we felt the more concern. It would seem as though Queen Mary persecuted most in the eastern part of England. And what could an Anabaptist do for the cause of religious freedom but plead for soul-liberty, and die?

This Richard Woodman, the Baptist ironmonger, had for a curate or minister of the parish a man who, in the days of our king, Edward VI., when Protestantism, but not religious liberty, held sway, had outwardly been a Protestant. But as soon as the Catholic Queen Mary came to the throne, the minister, whose name was Fairbanke, turned and became a Catholic, and taught the people the very opposite of that which he had before preached.

When Richard Woodman heard this teaching from his pastor's lips, he could not help speaking about it. And on this, Richard Woodman was immediately arrested and put in prison for a year and a half. There was religious freedom for an Anabaptist! Then Woodman was sent to that memorable place, Bishop Bonner's coal house, was examined and released, but was afterward unjustly arrested again, while ploughing. How- ever, he escaped and hid in the woods. Afterward he left England, but soon came back again, long- ing for his homeland.

By the treachery of his brother and father, Woodman was arrested. He had various exami- nations. During one, Dr. Langdale, the bishop of Chichester's chaplain, asserted that if Woodman's child had died before baptism it would have been eternally lost.

"How think you?" asked Woodman. "Are all condemned who receive not the outward sign of baptism?"

"Yea," answered the doctor, "that they be."

"How prove you that?" questioned Woodman, and Langdale answered by repeating the Lord's words promising eternal life to such as believe and are baptized, and condemnation to such as do not believe.

"Then," went on Woodman, "by your saying that baptism bringeth faith and all that are bap- tized in water shall be saved, shall they?"

"Yea, that they shall," returned the doctor; "if they die before they come to discretion, they shall be saved, every one of them; and all that be not baptized shall be damned, every one of them."

Then Woodman, greatly aroused that a man should say anything so contrary to the word of God as that baptism should save one, cried out : "How dare you speak such blasphemy against God and his word, as you do? How dare you for your life take upon you to preach and teach the people and understand not what you say? For I protest before God that you understand not the Scriptures, but as far as natural reason can comprehend ; for if you did, you would be ashamed to speak as you do."

Woodman challenged Dr. Langdale to prove his doctrine by Scripture, and the doctor turned pale and trembled. Then Woodman went on to show that Christ's words foretell condemnation to those who believe not.

Woodman, farther on in his examination, said to the doctor : "But you say that if they are baptized with the water, if they die before they come to the years of discretion they are all saved ; the which St. Peter is clean against, unless you grant that children have faith before they are baptized. Now I ask you, what consent of conscience the children have, being infants? For you say they believe not before they are baptized ; therefore, then, they consent not to be baptized, because they believe not. And by this it followeth that none shall be saved, although they are baptized. I would fain see how you can answer this."

And Langdale answered : "You are the most perverse man that ever I knew. You know not what you say. The children are baptized in their godfathers' and godmothers' faith, and that is the good conscience of which St. Peter speaks."

So argued they till Langdale began to stamp the floor, railing at Woodman. The examination continued, and there were six examinations in all, to which Woodman was subjected. During the fifth examination the bishop of Winchester threatened any man who would be kind to Woodman. There were more than three hundred people present at the examination, and the cruel bishop cried : "If any of you bid God strengthen him, or take him by the hand, or embrace him, or show him a cheerful countenance, you shall be excommunicated, and shall not be received again till you have done open penance ; and therefore beware of it."

This, I suppose, was spoken more particularly to the men of the bishop's diocese.

At the last examination the wicked bishop of Winchester said to the prisoner : "Thou art a heretic, and therefore thou shalt be excommunicated."

Woodman denied being a heretic, but no credence was given to his words.

"And so," wrote this Baptist after his last examination, while he was waiting his execution, "he read forth the sentence in Latin, but what he said God knoweth, and not I. God be judge between them and me. When he had done, I would have talked my mind to them, but they cried out,

'Away, away with him!' So I was carried to
the Marshalsea again; where I now am, and shall
be, as long as it shall please God. And I praise
God most heartily that ever he hath elected and
predestinated me to come to so high a dignity as
to bear rebuke for his name's sake; his name be
praised therefore for ever and ever. Amen."

Richard Woodman was burned with nine other
Christians, all in the same pile, four of the persons
being women, one of whom was very old indeed.
Time was not even allowed for a writ authorizing the burning to come down from London to
Lewes, in Sussex, where the martyrdom took
place. Truly we were made to feel that England
was no realm of religious liberty.

But this we had known for some time. Only,
after I had put together the things we must carry,
and after we took our little six-years-old boy and
went forth into the world, fugitives again, I looked
up at the sky and I thought of my baby Hendrick. He was safe, safe from bloody Queen
Mary and all her prelates. He was in a land of
religious freedom.

By as swift journeying as our feet could make
—though it was slow enough, and all too slow to
our hearts that far outstripped our footsteps—we
came at last to the town of Sandwich, which lies,
as is well known, on the coast of Kent upon the
edge of the North Sea, and at the mouth of the
river Stour.

Our hearts misgave us lest we should be too

late, and Stephen dared not have waited for our coming. But we found him and Thyra hidden in the house of a woman who feared God more than she feared our queen. And being received into the house and also hidden, we consulted what should be done.

"Let us leave England," advised Stephen. "Well I know the thoughts that lurk under a monk's cowl. I am sure the friars will kill Thyra and me if we abide in England. Oh, Gaspar, will religious freedom never come to the earth?"

Stephen told of several attempts that had already been made to take him.

"England is no safe place for an Anabaptist," declared Thyra. "One may not even call one's self by the right name, and say 'Baptist.'"

Long and earnestly we talked that night, and Gaspar, with the sound of the North Sea lingering it would seem yet in his ears, yielded to Stephen's importunity, and agreed to flee with them.

"If we could gain Germany," suggested Stephen; "or if we could reach Moravia."

Such were our plans; but, alas! when could fugitives choose their own ships, or their own ports? We waited, our friend's husband trying, greatly at his own risk, to find among the vessels of Sandwich one that would take us on board. Finally he discovered a ship-master who would conceal us, but the ship was bound for Rotterdam. Must we try the Low Countries again? Was England worse?

Perhaps we would have rejected the offer and stayed, at whatever risk, but that night there came men hunting through the town for Stephen. A monk directed the searchers, and they ransacked the place where Stephen and Thyra had lived, and with threats sought to discover whither "Brother Barnabas" had betaken himself. But us the monk and his helpers did not find.

So, being sure that death was determined for Stephen, and being unwilling that we should be separated, the next night we committed ourselves to God's care, and were hidden on board the ship for Rotterdam. And though Gaspar did not know what might come to us in the Low Countries, yet to him it was going home to his native land, and he could not but feel glad that he was so soon to see once more the dykes and meres of Holland. Fisherman that he had once been, the dull weaving that had since been his English occupation had ill suited him, and the sea air and the sound of the water seemed to send a thrill of exhilaration through his soul. He and Stephen talked much of the manner in which they hoped to find their way from Rotterdam into Germany.

"Oh," sighed Stephen, "will the day never come when in all these fair countries there shall be religious freedom? How happily might each of us serve God, if his neighbor would allow it! Why is it that religious liberty is so high a doctrine for men to attain to?"

Gaspar smiled a little sadly.

"Have patience with men, brother," he rejoined. "Our Lord has taught us Anabaptists that it is right that no compulsion should be used in matters that concern a man's conscience. But in all men there is not this knowledge. All men, though some may be learners of Jesus Christ, have not attained to the spiritual wisdom that the Anabaptists hold in this matter. And therefore it behooves us, as we have received this truth, to impart it to others, and to valiantly argue with men for the right of religious freedom for all."

"I trow that no other people have so bravely stood for religious freedom as have the Anabaptists," answered Stephen.

The first news we heard, on our arrival at Rotterdam, was of the death of that emperor whose decrees had caused Anabaptists in the Low Countries so much persecution. Charles V. was dead! He had died in the monastery of St. Yuste, in Spain.

"But Philip lives," the shipmaster warned us. "Think not that you can read your Bibles in peace. Did not the dead emperor forbid all reading of the Scriptures in the Netherlands?"

"Should an Anabaptist listen to such a command?" returned Gaspar. "Is it not the Anabaptists who have helped to spread the Bible in the past?"

"But Anabaptists must keep quiet now," rejoined the shipmaster cautiously. "Look you.

The emperor's ears are dead, but his son's—they listen."

Charles V., in the codicil to his will, conjured his son Philip most earnestly to follow up and bring to justice every heretic in his dominions, without showing any mercy to any one; and also to cherish the Holy Inquisition as the best instrument for exterminating heretics.

" So," concluded Charles, "shall you have my blessing, and the Lord shall prosper all your undertakings."

After years were to tell how carefully Philip followed this advice.

This year of his father's death, Philip published an edict in Spain, borrowed from an edict in the Netherlands, condemning all who bought, sold, or read prohibited works, to be burned alive. The son was worthy of his father.

But how terribly self-deceived Charles V. must have been. He left a testimony behind him that would make one think him a most devout Christian, if one did not know his bloody deeds. This was the testimony: "I have tasted more satisfaction in my solitude in one day, than in all the triumphs of my former reign. The sincere study, profession, and practice of the Christian religion have in them such joys and sweetness as are seldom found in courts and grandeur."

And yet Charles adjured his son Philip to cherish the Holy Inquisition. Verily the depths of self-deception in a human soul are wonderful.

For two days the funeral obsequies of the dead emperor were held at Brussels. A grand procession swept through the streets. The most conspicuous thing in the procession was a ship that seemed to float upon the waves. The masts, the shrouds, and the sails of the ship were black, and the ship was covered with banners and heraldic signs, in memory of Charles' expeditions. And whom should the ship have for crew but Hope, Faith, and Charity.

Hope, Faith, and Charity for *him!* For that emperor who had published the edicts in the Netherlands; who had sent Inquisitors among us, and who at last, when about to die, had adjured his son Philip by his hope of salvation to deal to all heretics the extreme rigor of the law, "without respect of persons and without regard to any plea in their favor."

On the second day of the obsequies, King Philip, dressed in mourning, went to the church where service was held, and Charles V. was solemnly announced to be dead.

To bring to "justice" every heretic in the Low Countries, that was the determination of King Philip. And not only did he himself determine it, but he entered into a secret league with the French king, Henry II., that they would exterminate by fire and sword all Protestants in their realms.

Now must I tell you, in this hour when the enemies of God were plotting to destroy every

one of us, how the Lord raised us up help even,
seemingly from our enemies. William the Silent,
Prince of Orange, had been highly recommended
to Philip II., our king, by his father, Charles V.
And Philip seemed inclined to make use of the
young man. William was sent, with the Duke of
Alva, and two other persons, to France. The
four were to be hostages sent by Spain, as a guar-
anty for the fulfillment of a treaty.

1559   While William was there, one day while
A.D.   hunting in the forest of Vincennes, very in-
cautiously the French king, Henry II., probably
supposing that so noted a young man had been
told before of the secret league between him and
the Spanish monarch, spoke to William of the
plan to kill all the Protestants. William was
horrified by the revelation, but knew better than
to show his horror and surprise to Henry.
William was silent. From that very hour his
purpose was fixed. He felt what he would do.
A little while afterward he came to the Low
Countries, and tried to excite the people against
having the Spanish troops there.

For William already felt, as he said, that "an
inquisition for the Netherlands had been resolved
upon more cruel than that of Spain, since it
would need but to look askance at an image to be
cast in the flames." And though William yet did
not believe as the Protestants did, he said he
could not "but feel compassion for so many vir-
tuous men and women thus devoted to massacre."

So William the Silent—thus called because he had kept still when the French king told of the purpose—determined to save these poor Christians if he could. He, a Catholic, would save us.

In one of the last talks that William had with Philip before leaving, the king had given him the names of several "excellent persons of the new religion," and had commanded that they be put to death. I do not know who they were, but I do know that instead of killing them, William gave them warning so that they might escape.

I have said that William was at this time a Catholic. When he was a little boy he was brought up in the Lutheran faith, but Charles V., being displeased that the boy should be so taught about religion, obtained the consent of William's parents that he should be taken to Brussels to live in the family of the emperor's sister, Regent Mary of Hungary. This, of course, was a Catholic family. William was only twelve years old when he went there. Who would have thought that God intended that in the future William should be the friend and defender of the Anabaptists, the champion of religious liberty? No one in that Catholic family surely. When William was fifteen years old he was made a page of Charles V.

But when, in after days, William came to the Low Countries with those names of "excellent persons suspected of the new religion," I think that his religious ideas were, perhaps, unsettled. However, he knew he was sorry for the good peo-

ple in trouble, and believed in religious liberty
enough to try to save them. One writer wrote of
William at one time in his career: "The Prince
of Orange passed for a Catholic among Catholics,
a Lutheran among Lutherans. If he could he
would have had a religion compounded of them
both. In truth, he looked on the Christian religion like the ceremonies which Numa the Roman
introduced as a sort of politic invention."

But the man who wrote that was unfriendly to
William. I know this, that the Prince of Orange
believed in religious freedom, and condemned persecution in matters of faith. He thought that all
men ought to be free in such matters. It was so
strange, so rare a thing to find any besides the
Anabaptists who really believed in religious freedom for all men, that I cannot but have faith that
God raised up William the Silent and sent him to
the Low Countries to aid us in our great troubles.
God was answering the prayers of the Anabaptists for religious freedom for all.

William was appointed governor of Holland,
Zealand, Utretcht, and West Friesland, and he had
been reminded that whereas some persons had im-
agined the severity of the law "to be only intended against Anabaptists, on the contrary the
edicts were to be enforced on Lutherans and all
other sectaries without distinction."

This shows how cruelly the Anabaptists had
been treated in the Low Countries. Alas, the
cruelties were by no means over!

Margaret of Parma was made regent of the Netherlands about this time. She was the half-sister of King Philip, and we knew how Spanish hands had treated Anabaptists in the past. Still she was a woman not wholly of Spanish blood, and we hoped for what we might. But, oh, what terrors followed, and what a mistaken man had she in her State Council. The Frisian, Viglius van Aytta van Zuichem, was one of the Council. He was a learned man, and he thought that for a common person who was not learned in law or divinity to enter into his closet, to shut the door, and to secretly pray to God was to open wide the gate of destruction for all in the land, and to bring in the Father of Evil at once to fly away with the souls of all the people.

None of us were to believe the contrary of the Catholic religion. The Regent Margaret was an enthusiastic Catholic. She had a greater horror of " heretics " than of any other sort of evildoers, and she looked up to the bloody edicts of her father, Charles V., as if they had been special revelations from heaven.

Viglius, that member of Margaret's State Council whom I have mentioned, was a most bigoted man. He regarded religious liberty as the most detestable and baleful of doctrines, and he thought "heresy" the most unpardonable of crimes. He would say the most bitter things against those blackest of malefactors, as he thought them, the men who claimed that within their own homes men had a right to worship God according to their own consciences.

So it may well be seen that, inasmuch as we Anabaptists believe in religious liberty for all men, our belief was directly opposed to that of Viglius, and none of us could hope for much favor at his hands. We should not worship God in the manner which we believed the Bible to command.

"This vague, fireside liberty should be by every possible means extirpated," declared Viglius.

He was president of the council of Mechlin, and it was to that town that Philip II. sent a letter giving instructions that the decrees for burning, strangling, and burying alive should be carried out to the letter. Not only were Anabaptists to be treated so, the king said, but all persons spotted with Luther's errors.

All we could do was to be thankful that Mechlin was between sixty and seventy miles to the south of us, and to hope that the State Council might not move particularly against the Anabaptists of Rotterdam; for we were there still, not finding how we might flee the width of Holland. We had obtained work and endeavored to keep ourselves hidden as much as possible, for we knew our danger, and I often thought of that company of Anabaptists, of whom I have told you, who were killed in Rotterdam fourteen years before this, having been betrayed by a woman who pretended that she came to borrow a kettle.

Our little boy, Eliezer, six years old now, was very fond of singing, and the hymn he sang most was that composed by the converted nun, Elizabeth, who became an Anabaptist and was drowned therefor. Her hymn was left to us though, and I used to often hear my little boy sing :

> " In thanks to God will I delight,
> And love and praise with all my might,
> Honor and fear him day and night.''

When I heard him sing that, I used so often to think of the answers of Elizabeth to the council that questioned her.

"What do you hold concerning infant baptism, that you should have had yourself baptized again?"

"No, gentlemen, I have not been baptized again ; I was baptized once on my confession of faith ; for it is written that baptism belongs to believers."

"Are our children then lost because they have been baptized?" questioned the council.

"No, gentlemen," replied Elizabeth ; "far be it from me that I should condemn children."

"Do you not expect salvation from baptism?" the questioners continued.

"No, gentlemen," returned the young Anabaptist. "All the waters in the sea cannot save me ; but salvation is in Christ ; and he hath commanded me to love the Lord my God above all things, and my neighbor as myself."

She was brought to the torture-tower and tortured with iron screws, so that she fainted, but she would not recant nor tell who it was that baptized her. And she was drowned. Could I have grace enough to follow if the trial came to me?

"My grace is sufficient for thee."

I remembered the words of the New Testament. And still my little boy sang on:

> " In thanks to God will I delight,
> And love and praise with all my might,
> Honor and fear him day and night."

CHAPTER XVII

STEPHEN AND THYRA DISAPPEAR

"I SAW a Benedictine monk to-day," whispered Thyra to me. "Oh, Editha, I am sure his face was English!"

There were very troublous times about us, and Thyra and Stephen left us and fled. We would have followed, but we were arrested and taken to prison. Our jailer taunted us with the condition of Anabaptists in the Low Countries, and whenever he heard of a particularly atrocious deed done to any of our faith, he spared no pains to tell us of it. He it was who told us, with great appearance of satisfaction, that Menno Simons, our good Anabaptist preacher, was dead. And it was through him that we learned how terrible beyond description were the deeds done in Flanders to those of the reformed religion, and to those who were Anabaptists. We hardly knew whether to believe the tales, so dreadful were they, but certain things we felt must be true, so real did the jailer make them in rehearsing them to us.

We were greatly alarmed, for Stephen and Thyra had betaken themselves to Flanders. We heard terrible tales of the things done by the Inquisitor, Peter Titelman, he who seemed to revel in blood, and who galloped through the country by night and by day, dragging suspected persons from their firesides and beds, putting people into dungeons, arresting, torturing, strangling, burning, without scarce waiting for trial or information.

"He says himself that he rarely waits for deeds," the jailer told us.

Suspicion was enough.

A certain schoolmaster, named Geleyn de Muler, of Audenarde, used to read the Bible, and Titelman summoned him and accused him of heresy. The schoolmaster claimed that if he were guilty of any crime, he should be tried before the judges of his town.

"You are my prisoner," answered Titelman, "and are to answer me and none other."

And the schoolmaster was strangled and thrown into the fire.

About the same time a tapestry weaver of Tournay, Thomas Calberg, was convicted of having copied some hymns from a book printed at Geneva. For this deed he was burned alive.

But there came to us a tale of the fate of two Anabaptists, and this alarmed us more than ever. Certain things made us fear that the two were Stephen and Thyra. The story told of the two Anabaptists, whoever they were, was a terrible one. They being taken prisoners, one of the soldiers had fallen upon the man with a rusty sword, dealing him one blow after another, cutting him to death. At this horrible sight, the wife—whom we could not doubt to be Thyra—gave a great cry, and dropped senseless. When one came to lift her, she was found to be dead also.

Gaspar asked me if I thought Thyra would die in that way.

" She seemed always of a stauncher nature than he," argued my husband, unwilling to believe his sister dead. "Would she die even at so dreadful a sight?"

" She loved him," I answered.

And indeed I cannot well explain how it is, but I know that sometimes when a strong, brave woman perceives that her husband is not so strong and brave as she, there is added to her love for him a tender pity, akin to the pity of a mother, and she loves him yet the more. And so, though I do not rightly or clearly express myself, never being a person of much mastery over words, I know how Thyra felt. She loved Stephen to the end. The sword that killed him pierced her heart also, though the weapon did not touch her. Gaspar was Thyra's brother, but I felt that I understood her better than he.

"If that Anabaptist was Stephen, I am sure it was some Benedictine monk who killed him," said Gaspar.

I did not answer, for I was thinking of the terrible tales I had heard of Peter Titelman, that very infamous Inquisitor. What was human life to the Inquisitors, who would burn men, women, and children, and throw away their ashes, for words spoken perhaps idly years before against Rome, or for praying alone in their closets, or for not kneeling to a wafer when meeting it in the street, or even for having had thoughts which had never been spoken aloud by the persons, but which on inquiry they were too honest to deny having had. Truly, the cruelty of the Inquisition was appalling.

And now, whether it was that Stephen and Thyra were the two Anabaptists who fell thus inside Peter Titelman's bloody domain, or whether my cousin and his wife perished in some other fashion, I know not. I can write no more of them in this chronicle, for they never were seen again by us. Yet am I sure that in the list of martyrs known in heaven are the names of Stephen and Thyra.

Within a few days we were taken from our prison to another and told that we should prepare ourselves for death. There was another jailer and it was he who made the announcement to us, though I think our former guardian would have enjoyed telling us that news as well as he had enjoyed imparting to us other information. But the second jailer told us our sentence with unconcern, as being a man who had done such a thing so often that he hardly cared to look to see how we received the words. Having told us he went away.

After so much of the constant alarm and worry

of hiding, I think Gaspar and I almost experienced a feeling of relief to know that the end was so near and that we should all die together.

As I walked the floor of our new cell I discovered in it a small hole, and no sooner had I stepped so as to darken the hole than confused cries came from somewhere below. I took my foot from the hole and dropped on my knees beside it.

" Bread ! bread ! "

There were women's voices that moaned this one word, that wailed it, that sobbed it. There were men's voices that repeated the magic word over and over as if hardly knowing what they said.

" Bread ! bread ! bread ! "

The voices were in numerous keys, but all together they were but as the sound of a chorus that dies away for lack of strength. Once the sound may have been loud enough, but now it was faint with exhaustion.

Gaspar and I had a little bread and some cheese about us, having brought the food from the other prison.

We dared not throw all down to the starving prisoners but we threw some, and there ensued such sobbing cries that we could scarcely endure them. We were obliged to hear them the longer because of the hole's smallness, which compelled us to break the bread and the cheese before throwing them down.

"Bread! bread!" the voices still sobbed hoarsely, and Eliezer burst into tears.

"Give them mine, mother," he whispered.

I looked at Gaspar.

"We shall be killed to-morrow," I said. "We can go without this."

So we threw down all that remained save a little that Gaspar insisted on keeping for ourselves. It was well he did so, as matters went afterward; but I could not have kept a crust, for every little while all night long I heard a moan from below that sounded like "Bread!"

Oh, the long, dark hours in which I listened to those dreadful moans! Gaspar had tried to obtain some information from those wretched prisoners as to who they were, and had succeeded in ascertaining that a large number of them were brethren of Anabaptist belief.

The next day we were visited by a man who informed us that we were destined to die that night.

"Then we shall spend to-morrow morning in heaven," answered Gaspar intrepidly, and the man went away.

As he went I recalled to my mind what my father had once declared concerning the persecutions of the Anabaptists: "Yea, but our persecutions will work out the religious freedom not only of ourselves, but of all other men."

If God might grant it! Surely he heard the prayers of the Anabaptists for religious freedom.

But it had not come yet. I remembered that King Philip once wrote a letter in which he said: "Rigorous and severe measures are the only ones to be employed in matters of religion. It is by fear only that the rabble can be made to do their duty, and not always then." Would religious freedom be granted while King Philip lived?.

Night came. At least we should all die together. The moans from the apartment below were very faint. There did not seem to be so many voices as before. The cry of "Bread" had subsided into unintelligible murmurs. We threw down a little bread, thinking since we must surely now die it would not matter if we went hungry to death. But no notice was taken, in the room below, of our gift. The prisoners seemed to be too weak to understand, and some voices that had been strongest the night before were altogether missing now, wherefore we conjectured that some of our fellow-prisoners might have been taken away to death without our knowledge.

We sat patiently waiting for the coming of the executioners. As our little amount of bread had been taken no notice of below, we did not throw down any more, and, our own hunger growing upon us as the night passed, we divided the last of our food and ate it. And still we waited. Midnight must be near.

"Are you afraid, my Eliezer?" I asked my boy.

He answered : " No, my mother.   I am ready."

"It is but a little way," I said.   And I did not say more, for I knew that my boy was a true Christian and was " ready," as he declared himself to be, though he was but young.

We waited.   The dark hours were so long.   It must be midnight.   Why did the executioners delay ?

It was dim morning when we heard steps.   Our door was opened and we were bidden to come out for examination before our accusers.

In an open space near the prison, we found a company of our fellow-prisoners assembled.   We were hastened away with threats of burning.

And now we came all to the spot where we were to be offered up.   Two men were bound to one stake, and fagots being piled about them, the wood was lit, and the smoke rose around the heads of the martyrs.   To hasten the flames one of the executioners went near the pile, and as he worked mocked those in the fire.   But no answer came.

The flames shot up more brightly and another martyr went into the presence of his King.

And then, one after another of our company of prisoners was taken to the stake.   We seemed to be in regular order.   Gaspar, and Eliezer, and I, were toward the last of the line.   Two women were led toward the stakes.   There were now seven other prisoners before me.

As the two women were set on fire, the flames

caught the garment of one of the executioners. Perhaps some inflammable substance, as pitch, or somewhat else, may already have been on his garb, for it suddenly flamed up as I never saw cloth before, and the men who guarded us sprang to put out the fire.

In that instant of confusion my husband and Eliezer grasped my hands, and we sped away. Not until we had gained a good distance did we hear a cry behind, as of men who had discovered our departure. And not ours alone, I think, for I had heard other swift footsteps that fled when we escaped.

At first I had no thought but that we would be taken. But the darkness of the morning favored us, and perhaps the burns of the executioner were considerable and delayed the soldiers, for we distanced them entirely, and then, hiding under an overturned small boat that had been left beside a half-dry mere, we remained concealed throughout the entire day without anything to eat. Had we not had that food to eat during the night before, I know well that I, at least, would not have had strength to outrun our enemies.

As we hid beneath the boat we consulted as to where we would flee if we might attain the border of Holland. We thought of Zealand. We thought of German cities. We even thought of Moravia, the land where so many Swiss Anabaptists had now and formerly taken refuge. England was not to be thought of by Anabaptists as a land of

freedom, for though Queen Mary was dead Queen
Elizabeth was an enemy of Anabaptists.

When darkness came we crept from beneath our
providentially provided cover, and, looking fearfully around to see that we were not pursued, journeyed as far as we could under hiding of the dark.
A peasant woman of whom we besought food
gave us some without asking any questions,
though I think she suspected what we might be.
But she had a little boy of her own, and she
looked at Eliezer, and I thought it was for our
child's sake that she gave us bread.

We dared not return to Rotterdam, but fled forward till we came to Utrecht. Penniless we
entered into that city, knowing that those who
arrested us at Rotterdam had no doubt taken our
scanty goods. The world seemed very lonesome
without Stephen and Thyra.

But perhaps this world would not be ours very
much longer. I thought of what King Philip
wrote last year to a bishop : " There are but few
of us left in the world who care for religion. 'Tis
necessary, therefore, for us to take the greater
heed for Christianity."

Verily King Philip thought he did God service!
So, at least, his words implied. Perhaps his
soldiers might yet lay hands upon Gaspar and
myself, and prove by our death that King Philip
" cared for religion " ! Philip little thought that
religious liberty might spring from the graves of
" heretics."

CHAPTER XVIII

CONTINUED DANGER

IN Utrecht and in neighboring villages we concealed ourselves from our persecutors, and worked as diligently as we could. We found in Utrecht an Anabaptist man who had helped his poorer brethren before this, and who gave Gaspar work, and us such protection as was possible. This friend had some possessions, and was loath to lose them all by flight to another country, though he and we often consulted as to which land an Anabaptist would be most safe in, were he forced to leave the Low Countries.

Still we stayed, for it seemed as if such terrible times for Anabaptists would not be permitted to keep on forever. And still the days of trial continued, and we kept ourselves hidden and unknown, almost, to our neighbors. It seemed wonderful to us that we could so stay in the Low Countries, in the very grasp as it were of our enemies, and yet be kept from death. It was only through the overshadowing hand of our God that we were thus hidden. I realized that, as day by day we worked on, and I looked at my husband and at Eliezer, and thought how marvelously we three, whose hearts would be so torn by a separation from one another, were kept, a little family, still together.

But when I remembered all the past—when I thought of the fagot pile at Caversham, and of the night on which my father was nearly captured, and my mother and I went forth, terrified wanderers in the dark; when I recalled that long waiting beside the wall, praying that father might come; when I remembered our flight through the sheep, and the nearness of our bloodthirsty enemies and the manner in which we had all escaped from England to the Low Countries, I felt that the God who had guided us then, watched still over Gaspar, Eliezer, and me. How could I doubt that the deliverance of the Lord had been with me, when I remembered the escape of Thyra and me from the prison where we had seen the strangled Anabaptist and the dying priest, or when I remembered my life in the village of Scheveningen, and my narrow escape from burial at the hands of the soldier, or when I thought of the ten years in prison, and our flight and deliverance from the purpose of Johannes, the traitor? When I recalled so many perils and narrow escapes as had filled my life, I was wont to question myself: "Cannot God keep us now?" and so try to cast my care on him.

And I would comfort myself by thinking of that promise of the New Testament: "If two of you shall agree on earth as touching anything that they shall ask, it shall be done for them of my

Father which is in heaven." Were there not many of us Anabaptists who prayed for religious liberty? Had not some of us agreed to pray that liberty of soul might come to all men, in the Low Countries and elsewhere? Was not that the burden of our prayers, and would not God hear? Was prayer nothing?

Our boy Eliezer was growing up a fine, earnest lad. He was thirteen during those years we stayed in Utrecht and the neighboring villages, and he often listened to his father's tale of the boy-martyr, the young Anabaptist Jaques Dosie, who, though only fifteen years old, had witnessed a good confession, and had been put to death over in Friesland a few years before this. The wife of the governor of Friesland was interested in the young boy, and Gaspar would tell Eliezer what questions the lady asked of Jaques, and what answers the boy gave. I remember once hearing Gaspar say: "The governor's wife asked Jaques, 'Are you not one of the people who rebaptize themselves, and do so much evil in our country, exciting uproar, running together, and who say that for their faith they are driven away, and boast of being the church of God; but who are a dangerous set, and make great disturbance among the people?'

"But Jaques answered: 'My lady, tumultuous people. I know none, and am in no wise of the number of such; but we desire much rather, as the Scripture teaches us, to assist our enemies, and

S

if they are hungry or thirsty to satisfy them with food and drink, and in no wise to resist them by violence or to avenge ourselves.'

" The lady asked : ' Were they not your people who disgracefully and shamefully took up the sword against the magistrates at Amsterdam and Münster ? "

"'Oh, no, madam,' returned Jaques ; ' those persons greatly erred.   But we consider it a devilish doctrine to resist the magistrates by the outward sword and violence.   We would much rather suffer persecution and death at their hands, and whatever is appointed us to suffer.'

" And afterward the lady asked the boy : ' Do you not think that all are lost who are not baptized in your way ? '

"'Oh, no, madam,' answered Jaques again. ' Judgment belongs to God alone, who will reward every man according to his works, as plainly appears in many places of the Holy Scriptures. Besides, water has no power to cleanse us from sin, as Peter says ; but is only a token of obedience.'

" And in answer to some question, Jaques said too : ' Concerning the use of infant baptism, we speak with reason against it, as being no command of Almighty God ; but much rather an invention of men, considering that the young children have no knowledge or discernment about whatever is required and contained in the baptismal service.   But Christ, from affection to such innocents, without their seeking it themselves, graciously promised them the kingdom of God.'

"The lady told him that she considered the worst in the Anabaptists to be their refusal to baptize children. 'For all Germany, and every kingdom,' said she, 'regard your conduct as heresy.' And Jaques answered: 'Madam, such is indeed the truth, that we are everywhere contemned, and are, like the apostolic band, spoken against in all the world; but do not think that all such will therefore in the last day be lost.'

"And so, although the lady besought him to repent of his baptism, saying that it would be a heavy cross to her heart if so young a child as he should die, yet the boy Jaques was steadfast, declaring: 'Madam, in my baptism I can find nothing criminal, considering that herein I have followed not my own will, but the institution of our Lord Jesus Christ.'"

So did the boy die, being put to death by those who would not suffer him to have religious liberty.

Eliezer used to listen to the tale, and I thought he pondered it so gravely afterward that I was moved with fear lest a premonition that martyrdom was to be his own end had come to him. I shrank from such a belief, and I wished he and his father would not talk so much of Jaques Dosie.

But a new year dawned, and matters changed. In this year there came unexpected news. Liberty of worship was granted the "new religion." The Inquisition was said to be done away. 1566 A.D.

Had liberty indeed come? We Anabaptists looked at one another in amazement. If the Reformed had religious freedom, possibly Anabaptists might be treated less cruelly.

"God has touched King Philip's heart," reverently murmured one woman.

Gaspar's face glowed.

"If liberty of conscience is granted," he exclaimed, "what a land will the Netherlands become! This dear land!"

And because he believed that liberty of worship would probably continue, and because I also had much faith that bright days had dawned, and that Philip, perceiving that the Catholic could never be the only religion of the Netherlands, had relented, we remained in the Low Countries.

Very peaceful and sweet was our dream of liberty, after so many years of danger.

"It is good that we brought our boy back to his father's country," Gaspar said, looking fondly at Eliezer.

And indeed England had been so hard a country to me, that I answered, "Yes, I am glad we have come back to the Low Countries."

But our dream of freedom soon ended. The next year we bewailed ourselves that we had not fled. At this time the Catholics were triumphant. Troops belonging to the regent rode over the country, and wherever the Reformed were 1567 gathered to hear the word, they were dis- A.D. turbed by the troopers, who trampled the people under the horses' hoofs, shooting persons down, or dragging them away by scores to execution. People either bribed the priests to keep silence, or else came compulsorily to mass. There were many who violated their consciences to save their lives. Along the roads, everywhere, bodies were hanging from gibbets, churches were pulled down, and people were hung from the beams.

The regent issued in May an edict sentencing all ministers and teachers to the gallows. All persons who had allowed their houses to be used for religious purposes were sentenced to the gallows. All people who sang hymns at the burial of any relative were sentenced to the gallows. It was made a capital crime to sneer against priests.

Such laws drove timid people, who dared not stand for their religion, into hypocrisy. Persons who for years had not gone to mass, now attended the Catholic services, morning and night. Persons who had scornfully spoken to Catholic ecclesiastics, now would not eat dinner without some priest at the table.

I shall never forget something I saw this year. Gaspar and Eliezer and I had fled from Utrecht for a time. In our wanderings we came to a place where a mere had been. Hearing voices, we concealed ourselves.

The mere had been drained, so that the soil was but a little damp. In what had once been the bed of the mere something terrible was transpiring. A company, apparently prisoners and their guards, stood there. Where we lay we could plainly hear the accusations cast upon the prisoners of being heretics and Münsterites. Some of our Anabaptist brethren without doubt stood there.

"The men are digging," whispered Gaspar to me.

It was too true. In five or six places the men were upturning the earth. Alas! We knew for what awful purpose this must be. Continually, as the guards waited to be relieved of their prisoners, there were to be heard mockings and cruel jests. I longed for the power of an army to come down into this mere and snatch the poor Anabaptist victims from the grasp of their heartless enemies.

There was a movement in the group below. It parted and two girls stood forth in front of the other persons. Those who had been digging one of the graves were waiting for something.

" Come !" sternly ordered a soldier.

I remembered how nearly I had been put to death once in this manner. The two young maidens took each other's hand and walked intrepidly forward. One of them began to sing triumphantly. I heard the words. They were those of Coverdale's hymn :

> Be glad now, all ye Christian men,
> And let us rejoyce unfaynedly.
> The kindnesse cannot be written with penne,
> That we have receaved of God's mercy;

Whose love toward us hath never end;
He hath done for us as a frende;
Now let us thanke him hartely.

These lovynge wordes he spake to me:
I wyll delyver thy soule from payne;
I am disposed to do for thee,
And to myne owne selfe thee to retayne.
Thou shalt be with me for thou art myne;
And I with thee, for I am thyne;
Such is my love, I cannot layne.

The clear, exultant voice never failed. Now, as the two girls were roughly pushed into a single, wide pit, and the soldiers stood ready to throw the earth upon the bright young martyr heads, both maiden voices arose in unison in the words that Coverdale represents our Lord as saying:

They will shed out my precyous bloude,
And take away my lyfe also,
Which I wyll suffre all for their good;
Beleve this sure, where ever thou go,
For I will yet ryse up agayne,
Thy synnes I beare, thought it be payne,
To make thee safe and free from wo.

The earth went hastily in. The executioners seemed eager to be through. But the girls began another hymn, heard spasmodically through the falling earth. It was the hymn of a martyr, and was sung in Dutch:

Of such a man fear not the will,
A body—only he can—kill,
A faithful God—thee rather fear,
Who—can—condemn to darkness drear.

O Christ—help through—thy little flock,
Who—faithful—follow thee—their Rock,
By thine—own death——

A soldier bent over the edge of the pit, and with his shovel dealt two savage blows on the fair heads below. When he drew his shovel up I fancied it was red.

More hurriedly than ever the earth went in. There was no sound but that of the falling gravel. The grave was filled and stamped till the ground was hard. The young Anabaptists were safe at last.

"They were English," I whispered to Gaspar.

A cry of agony rose from the mere. We looked and saw a man struggling with the guards who kept him back. He held out his arms toward a woman who was being led in the direction of another open grave.

"Oh, my wife! my heart! my life's love!" cried the man in Dutch.

The soldiers mocked him, but after the scornful laughter ceased, the woman's voice arose in the same language, clear, distinct, though she was being bound and might not turn her head to look at him: "My beloved, I shall see thee again in our Father's kingdom."

The woman was fastened into a coffin-like receptacle and thrown into the grave. Other women followed her. There were men who were evidently prisoners, but none of them were buried. They were probably brought there to cause them the agony of seeing their dearest buried alive. The stake or the multiplied ortures of the Inquisition awaited them.

The living burials went on. I wished that my boy need not have seen the sight. But after the first two graves were filled he threw his arms about me and hid his face on my shoulder so that he saw no more.

"If they should bury *you*, mother! If they should bury *you!*" he whispered. And I could feel him sob silently with the grief of one to whom a thought too terrible to be borne has come.

After I had quieted him I turned to Gaspar.

"My husband," I whispered.

He looked at me. The dear, patient kindness of those eyes! How much he and I had borne and suffered together! My heart was very full as I whispered my question.

"It is the same it used to be, Gaspar! Oh, my husband, where is the religious liberty that Anabaptists have striven and prayed for so long? It is not in England, it is not in the Low Countries!"

"My Editha," whispered Gaspar—and his whisper was tremulous with feeling—"religious liberty will rise from such graves as those of the buried Anabaptist women in that mere."

He pointed downward to where the awful sacrifice of human life went on.

"Can such fruits come from death?" my thoughts questioned one another. "How long,

O Lord, how long shall such things be? How long, O Lord, God of freedom, shall men cry out for religious liberty and see it not?"

A chant, as of those who sang with exceeding gladness, burst forth from below. The last four Anabaptist women advanced to the only grave that was now open.

"Be strong! Be strong! It is but the gateway of heaven!" cried an old man, a prisoner, as the women paused beside the grave.

"I shall rise again," triumphantly answered one of the women.

Then I thought there was a thrill of superstitious fear in the voice of the soldier, who shouted: "Anabaptist! Vile heretic! Be quiet!"

Perhaps he feared to meet sometime one who spoke so confidently of her resurrection.

But the chant rose again with its exceeding gladness, and the men prisoners added their voices.

"We ascend unto God," they all sang, "unto God, our Redeemer. Father, forgive our enemies."

The women were hastily thrown into the grave and buried. But the triumph of those chanting voices rang yet in my ears. The horror of the scene was almost obliterated so great had been the gladness with which those Anabaptists welcomed heaven.

Thrilled by what we were seeing and hearing we had hardly given more than a thought to our own safety. But now the soldiers drove their prisoners forward, though not quite in our direction. We lay crouching close to the ground, our hearts beating violently, fearing lest the soldiers should suddenly veer toward our hiding place. But they and their prisoners passed on.

"Oh, my Editha! my Editha!" groaned Gaspar; "why did I ever bring you to this country?"

I tried to comfort him by telling him that perhaps we might yet escape from it.

But he knew, as well as I, the royal ordinance that had been given forth that year : "It is forbidden to any one to leave the land, or to send off his effects, without obtaining a license from the authorities, under pain of being regarded as having taken part in the late troubles, and of being dealt with accordingly. All masters and owners of vessels who shall aid such persons in their flight, shall incur the same penalties."

The penalties were death and confiscation of property. Soon after the promulgation of this ordinance, ten of the principal merchants of Tournay were arrested and their estates were confiscated, because there was suspicion, probably well-grounded, that they were preparing to flee.

Moreover, it was decreed by our enemies, that whosoever fled from the Low Countries now might never return! To a man who loved his native land this was a hard thing.

"But some have fled in safety," I tried to cheer Gaspar. "Some have reached safety in Germany, and why not we?"

"My Editha," he answered heavily, his face yet against the ground, "if it is God's will!"

I was growing almost frightened about my husband in these days. His one thought seemed to be to protect his wife and his boy. A great melancholy seemed to have laid hold of Gaspar, and I feared lest his health should break with the strain.

Oh, if we could have fled! But flight was becoming almost impossible. The shipmasters and wagoners were afraid to assist any heretic to escape, though numbers of people had succeeded in leaving the Netherlands, even after the edict of May. Whether a person were a foreigner or a native of the Netherlands, however, he was forbidden to leave the country.

"If we could reach the Zuyder Zee! If we might flee across it to Embden!"

Such were our thoughts. We tried to bargain with a wagoner to conceal us in his wagon and carry us away as far as he would. But, although he agreed to do so, yet we discovered in time that he was a traitor, and only waited to deliver us into the hands of the priests.

With difficulty my husband and I made our way again northeastward to Utrecht. There we hid ourselves from the enemy as well as we could, and stayed for a time, seeing no way by which we might continue our journey eastward toward Germany.

The regent, the Duchess of Parma, resigned,

and at last left the Netherlands, toward the end
of this year. So did Margaret close her bloody
career among us.

Philip had written to his sister, the regent, saying : "I have never had any object in view than
the good of my subjects. In all that I have done
I have but trod in the footsteps of my father,
under whom the people of the Netherlands must
admit they lived contented and happy. As to the
Inquisition, whatever people may say of it, I have
never attempted anything new. With regard to
edicts, I have been always resolved to live and
die in the Catholic faith. I could not be content
to have my subjects do otherwise. Yet I see not
how this can be compassed without punishing the
transgressors. God knows how willingly I would
avoid shedding a drop of Christian blood—above
all, that of my people in the Netherlands ; and I
should esteem it one of the happiest circum-
stances of my reign to be spared this necessity."

And yet that bloody man, Alva, was after- 1567
ward sent to the Low Countries with an A.D.
army of about ten thousand veterans, and he
established that fearful tribunal of twelve judges,
called originally the " Council of his Excellency,"
but named by the people the " Council of Blood."
Surely Philip might have spared his " people in
the Netherlands " this.

While we were yet hiding at Utrecht a 1568
new year came. A most dreadful order was A.D.
issued in February, condemning the *entire popu-*

lation of the Netherlands, with but few exceptions, to death as heretics. The helpless people were doomed. The king ordered this death warrant to be executed at once, "without any hope of grace whatever, that it might serve for an example and a warning to all future time."

A new horror was added to the executions. To prevent the persons who were to be killed from addressing the people on the way, each prisoner's tongue was forced through an iron ring, and then burnt with a hot iron. This treatment caused the tongue to swell so that it became impossible to speak, especially as it was compressed between two plates of metal screwed fast together. The groans of the tortured men sounded strangely, and at one time in a company who looked at such a horror and heard the sounds, a friar cried out : "Hark, how they sing! Should they not be made to dance too ?"

During the four months ending the first of June, the persecution was most severe. Alva spoke of eight hundred victims, Viglius said that fifteen hundred were cited before the tribunal. To Philip, Alva had said that he wished that every man as he lay down at night, or as he rose in the morning, "might feel that his house at any hour might fall and crush him."

I think Alva obtained the meaning of his wish.

No wonder that many people wished to flee from the Netherlands. Queen Elizabeth of England had welcomed many Netherlanders who had fled to her realm, and had assigned them towns, as Sandwich, Norwich, and other places, where about thirty thousand emigrants from the Low Countries had been established. But alas! though Queen Elizabeth valued the mechanical skill of the people of the Low Countries, and the English were glad to be taught to make silk, and satin, and cloth, yet the queen was not a friend to Anabaptists, and early in this year the English bishops had obtained a proclamation from the queen directing a severe visitation to be made through London, and ordering all persons " that have conceived any manner of such heretical opinions as the Anabaptists do hold, and meaneth not by charitable teaching to be reconciled, to depart out of this realm within twenty days, upon pain of forfeiture of all their goods, and to be imprisoned and further punished."

Religious freedom had not yet come to England. And in our poor Low Countries it was common to see thirty or forty persons arrested at once.

In the dreadful state of affairs, following the order condemning all the Netherlanders to death, we looked to William the Silent for help. He strove to raise an army, but the expense was very great. The prince pawned his jewels and sent his plate to the mint. Nor was this all. Prince William announced his intention of expelling the Spaniards forever from the country. Money was very necessary to accomplish this great deed.

Prince William appealed to all his countrymen, even to those in poverty, to contribute toward this undertaking.

And, in this paper, Prince William quoted those three verses of Proverbs :

"The hope of the righteous shall be gladness : but the expectation of the wicked shall perish.

"The way of the Lord is strength to the upright : but destruction shall be to the workers of iniquity.

"The righteous shall never be removed : but the wicked shall not inhabit the earth."

It was a terrible war in which the Prince of Orange was about to engage. He had now brought together an army of nearly thirty thousand men. He wanted money for the war. And, alas ! how little money came in. Of three hundred thousand crowns promised by Marcus Perez, on behalf of the leading merchants and nobles of the Netherlands, but ten or twelve thousand came.

1568   Then was the hour for Anabaptist aid !
A.D.   Then a poor refugee congregation of Anabaptists remembered to help our prince, and an Anabaptist preacher risked his life to bring the small, hardly-spared sum of money to William's camp. Oh, the prince never forgot that !

Dissenting preachers, starving and persecuted church communities sent in contributions in course of time.

I think that William the Silent knew the Anabaptists better after that. He knew that Anabaptist hearts could be loyal to the cause of their country's freedom. Perhaps he may not in his earlier years have known how wholly Anabaptists believe in religious liberty for all men.

And I am proud to think that in the sorest strait in which a country might be, we of the Anabaptist faith proved ourselves right loyal men and women, who, even if we did not believe in war, yet held ourselves ready to pay for our substitutes, and to give freely all we could toward the release of our land from the grasp of Spain. Perhaps we might have seemed more brave had we thought the word of God allowed us to bear arms. And, verily, if there was ever a righteous war, it was this war with Spain. But let me say that it required more control of self, more denial of one's own feelings, not to rush to arms in these years of bitter persecution than it would have required to go. For Anabaptists had brave hearts, and it is not always easy to resist one's inclination to right one's own wrongs instead of waiting for the arm of the Lord.

It is a brave heart that dares obey God and take the risk of being called a coward by one's fellowmen. God save the Anabaptists from taking vengeance into their own hands.

Indeed, if we had believed in fighting, we might have been heroes in the eyes of worldly people, but I doubt whether we should have done deeds more thrilling, more heroic, than those that Anabaptists did do.

T

1569 A.D. It was in the next year that Dirk Willem-zoon, an Anabaptist who was guilty of no crime, but who had been baptized and had had meetings at his house, was escaping, after having been condemned to death. An officer of justice was pursuing Willemzoon, who fled across a frozen lake. The ice trembled and cracked beneath the Anabaptist's footsteps, but he reached the farther shore safely.

The officer who pursued was so unfortunate as to feel the ice give way beneath him. He fell through into the water, giving a cry for help.

Willemzoon could not leave his enemy to drown, and coming back across the dangerous ice, helped him to safety. But Willemzoon paid his life for the merciful deed.

Though the officer did wish to avoid the responsibility of murdering his preserver, yet the burgomaster of Asperen sternly reminded him to remember his oath. Thereupon the officer arrested Willemzoon, who was burned to death under the most lingering tortures.

But what could one expect when the Duke of Alva gave such dreadful instructions to the magistrates? Daily people were burned or hanged. The duke was very strict about the baptism of infants, it being ordered that the birth of every child should be reported within twenty-four hours in order that the Catholic baptism might be administered. Of course such an order would be particularly abhorrent to Anabaptist parents.

Moreover, the magistrates were ordered by the duke to appoint certain spies, who should keep watch at every administration of the sacraments and report any persons who did not pay suitable honor to the sacraments, such persons to be burned to death. But a most shocking order was that the same spies were to keep watch beside dying persons and give immediate notice to the government of all people who dared die without receiving extreme unction and the holy wafer. The estates of all such dead persons were to be confiscated, and their bodies dragged to the public place of execution.

In such times of peril many were the kindly deeds that even a persecuted Anabaptist might do, and often, when Gaspar and I were helping some poor dying Protestant, I have felt that perhaps this was one of the reasons why the Lord had allowed us to come to the Low Countries, that we might minister to his children, even though they might not be of the same faith as we were, and even though if we had been in their plight, they might have hesitated about relieving Anabaptists.

From one place to another we had gone, being unable to continue our eastward journey. We had hidden long at Utrecht, so long that we commenced to do business in a humble way, and had felt a certain sense of content, even in the midst of such dreadful times. One can grow used to almost anything.

At last we fled from Utrecht and wandered homeless again till finally we found our way to Leyden, and there, hidden as one sometimes can hide in a city, we tried to make our home. And so we were in Leyden the year when the Spanish army began its siege of that place. From the last of 1573-4 October till into the next March Leyden A.D. was besieged, and then, in order to meet the army of Louis of Nassau, brother of William the Silent, the Spanish army went away.

Great was our joy. We were quite certain we had nothing more to fear. Louis of Nassau would be victorious. The Spanish army would be routed. Or if it were not, almost five months of siege had taught the enemy the difficulty of taking our city. Surely we might trust our troubles were over, in great measure, from Spanish hands.

"Perhaps," I said to Gaspar, "when the Spaniards are defeated and driven from the land, the people of the Low Countries may have had so much trouble that we shall all live together in peace, and even Anabaptists may have religious liberty; for every person in this country might have freedom of conscience. Would not that be a glorious outcome of these dreadful years?"

"May God grant it," answered Gaspar devoutly. But his tone was not expectant.

CHAPTER XIX

THE SIEGE OF LEYDEN

" WHAT are the people calling?" I asked.

1574 A.D.

We listened.

Excited voices came to our ears.

" Count Louis is defeated!"

" Count Louis is dead!"

"Louis of Nassau has failed!"

" Count Henry is dead, and Duke Christopher!"

" Four thousand men were killed!"

" Some were slain on the field, some were suffocated in the marshes, some were burned in the farmhouses!"

Such were the wild rumors that flew through Leyden.

" The Spaniards will come back and attack us again," prophesied one man.

" Perhaps not," returned another. "There is mutiny among them. Three years' pay is due the soldiers."

" Leyden has her walls and her stout hearts," cried another citizen. " Know you surely that Count Louis is defeated?"

" It is the rumor," answered still another.

"Then sorrow fills the heart of the Prince of

Orange," returned the first man, "to lose a brother like Louis of Nassau."

We knew it was probable, unless the Spanish mutiny were too great, that the siege of Leyden would be begun again. The twenty-sixth of May the leader of our enemies, Valdez, reappeared before our city. The siege began. Valdez took the Hague, Maeslandshuis and Vlaardingen. Five hundred English abandoned the fortress of Valkenburg, and fled toward Leyden. But the men of our city, having good reason to distrust the English, refused to admit the five hundred inside Leyden. They surrendered to Valdez, and they afterward were sent to England.

"We should have taken the advice of the Prince to victual our city and strengthen the garrison, while we had time," groaned one man of Leyden as we faced the siege that was before us.

"Who would have thought that we would have to endure a second siege?" questioned another. "Who would have thought that Louis of Nassau would fail?"

We had surely cause for alarm. There were by this time no less than sixty-two redoubts girdling the city and we heard that the army besieging us already numbered nearly eight thousand men. These were daily added to by our enemies. And within Leyden, alas, what had we? Five companies of the burgher guard and a small corps of freebooters. What were they against our enemies? We had no troops save those I have mentioned.

And on Leyden depended the fate of all Holland, the fate not only of ourselves, but of generations to come. If we should fail, farewell to civil or religious liberty in these Netherlands. The critical hour had come. Now, if the prayers of Anabaptists ever ascended to the God of freedom, now was the time for them.

William the Silent sent a message to Leyden imploring the inhabitants to hold out at least three months, and assuring us that in that time he would find means to help us. He reminded us that we were not to contend for ourselves alone, but that the fate of our country and of unborn generations would, in all human probability, depend on the issue of this siege. Eternal glory would be our portion if we manifested a courage worthy of our race and of the sacred cause of religion and liberty.

" If this freedom from Spain and the Catholics is secured will the Lutherans let us Anabaptists have freedom?" asked an Anabaptist woman of me, doubtfully.

She had learned the bitter lesson that even Protestants can persecute Anabaptists. She dreaded lest there should come another tyranny upon our sect, though Spain and the Papists were repulsed.

" William the Silent will not forget what Anabaptists have done for him," I answered. " As certainly as William conquers in this war he will not allow others to persecute us, no matter what

Protestants may wish to do to us. I am certain of that."

And as after events showed my confidence in William the Silent was not misplaced. He never forgot that the Anabaptists had in his time of need given him out of their most bitter poverty the money they could. William believed in liberty for us as well as for the Reformed.

But now, while Leyden was in such straits, King Philip thought it time to try a treacherous plan of his. He issued a pardon, inviting all his repentant subjects to return to him and receive full forgiveness. The only condition that he imposed upon us was that we should all return likewise to the Mother Church. We were, with the exception of but a small number of persons who were mentioned, to be forgiven. We, who had been condemned to death.

But the people of Holland would not surrender to King Philip in this manner. They knew well how much faith that cruel man would keep with those whom he called "heretics." And though we Anabaptists did not believe in war, yet I think all our hearts beat faster when we heard of the brave saying of the Prince of Orange, after the second siege of Leyden had begun: "As long as there is a living man left in the country, we will contend for our liberty and our religion."

And would you know how many persons availed themselves of King Philip's offer of pardon? Two, only. One brewer of Utrecht and the son of a refugee peddler from Leyden. All Holland treated the king's offer with contempt.

Treacherous letters were sent into Leyden by certain Netherlanders who belonged to the king's party, and in these letters the citizens of our city were urgently, and sometimes pathetically, implored to submit to the king, and "to take pity upon their poor old fathers, their daughters, and their wives."

"Take pity upon them!" repeated Eliezer scornfully. "The best pity we can show to our fathers, our daughters, and our wives, is to keep them out of the hands of the Spanish soldiers."

And so thought the burghers of Leyden.

But our situation was now growing grave. By the end of June the people of our city were placed on a strict allowance of food. Before this our citizens had taken account of their provisions of all kinds, and of their livestock. The city authorities purchased all the provisions, and now half a pound of meat and half a pound of bread was allotted to each man, and some due proportion to the rest of us. We were so besieged that there could be no communication between us and the outside world, except by carrier pigeons, and by a few swift messengers called "jumpers."

One day I heard in the street the sound of a man's voice that sang loudly, in Dutch of course, some verses deriding the Inquisition.

There was silence for a few moments after he paused. Then an excited confusion of voices was

audible, and then the man's song began again.
Other rough voices sang with him. I could
plainly hear the words of another song, with
which I had grown familiar during the siege. A
favorite verse began with the words,

'T swaert is getrokken,

which mean in English :

The sword is now drawn.

I looked out, and a dreadful sight met my eyes.
A man of Leyden stood singing, holding aloft the
bloody, ghastly head of a Spaniard. I drew back,
unable to bear the sight of that grisly, blood-
stained head held aloft.

But the dreadful exultant voices went on outside.

Oh, the sword *was* taken! It was taken. But
was this the way that God meant religious liberty
to come? How could that man send an enemy
down to death unprepared? That Spanish soldier—where was his soul now? Would it not be
better that every Anabaptist, every Reformed person in the Netherlands, should be offered up in
martyrdom, being ready to die, than send one of
our enemies to eternity unprepared?

"*'T swaert is getrokken!*" shouted the triumphant voices.

The men went with the victor to obtain the
reward offered any man who brought in a Span-

iard's head. And I knelt there, horror-stricken, listening to the voices as they died in the distance.

"All they that take the sword shall perish with the sword."

Our Lord said it. Perhaps this Spanish soldier but received his due reward. Yet I hoped and prayed that no hands dear to me might ever be stained with the blood of an enemy. Anabaptists do not believe in war. It was a relief to me, and I doubt not to others, when the church bell was rung in Leyden, and it was forbidden that in future any man should leave the city gates. The authorities were becoming afraid lest the city, little by little, should lose its few disciplined defenders, in such sorties and combats as had been going on.

And so the days of our siege continued. Valdez, at the end of July, sent the citizens of Leyden most urgent and ample offers of pardon if we would open our gates and accept Philip's authority. But though we were almost at the point of starvation, we would not accept.

"Remember Haarlem!" whispered one to another, warningly. "Remember Naarden!"

We did remember. We remembered that starving, dying, gallantly resisting Haarlem had at last surrendered, because of a promise written in the name of Count Overstein, commander of the German forces in the besieging army, and sent by Don Frederic. The letter contained a solemn assurance that no punishment should be inflicted except upon those who, in the judgment of the citizens of Haarlem, had deserved it. Ample forgiveness was promised, if Haarlem would submit without delay. And yet at the very moment of sending that letter, Don Frederic knew that he had strict orders from his father not to leave a man alive in the garrison, except the Germans.

Haarlem surrendered. Five executioners, with their attendants, were kept constantly at work, and when they were exhausted, three hundred of the victims were tied two and two, back to back, and drowned in Haarlem lake. Twenty-three hundred murders were accomplished in that city before the treacherous "pardon" was allowed to be extended. That was the Spanish way of keeping a promise.

We did remember Haarlem. And we remembered Naarden. We remembered that Julian Romero agreed with the deputation from Naarden, and speaking in the authority commissioned him by Don Frederic, said that the lives and property of all the inhabitants of Naarden should be sacredly respected. To show that the promise was honest, Don Julian gave his hand three times to one of the men of the deputation from Naarden.

And that deputation, trusting in the Spanish promise, surrendered the keys of the city. All the housewives of Naarden went to preparing a great feast for the Spaniards. The Spaniards ate readily, and after the dinner the citizens were summoned to assemble in the Gast Huis Church, which was then used as a town hall. Five hundred people came there to hear what should be said to them.

A priest had been walking to and fro before the church door. Suddenly he walked into the building and bade the people prepare for death. A band of Spaniards sprang in, fired on the people, and then leaped upon them with daggers and swords. There was a great scream. It took but a few minutes. The very senator at whose table the Spanish commander had just been entertained was stricken down. All were killed and the church was set on fire.

The Spaniards rushed into the streets. The town was fired in every direction. The citizens rushed into the streets. Some people were chopped to pieces with axes. Horrors were enacted. Some hundred burghers escaped across the snow into the open country. They were overtaken, their clothing torn from them, and they were hung upon the trees by the feet to freeze or die a lingering death. Most of the burghers died. Nearly all the inhabitants of Naarden were killed. A little while afterward the city was razed to the ground. That was the Spanish way of keeping a promise.

We of Leyden would not be so deceived. The dead of Haarlem and Naarden were our warning, and though we did not know exactly what the Prince of Orange was doing, yet we chose to believe in William rather than in the Spanish.

" Better a drowned land than a lost land," the Estates had cried, at last giving their consent to William's plan of letting in the sea, and so coming to Leyden's relief.

We knew the Spaniards would be in consternation if the sea came. But in Leyden, alas! alas! How should we endure much longer? Our bread was gone. We ate malt cake, and we had little of that. The twelfth of August we had word from the prince, saying we should have speedy relief. It had need be speedy. The twenty-first we sent word to him that we had kept our promise, for we had held out two months with food, and another month without food.

Our malt cake would last but four days more, and then if no help came we must starve. We did not know that William was ill with a violent fever.

But on the very day on which this dispatch was sent from Leyden to Prince William, a letter was received by us saying that the dykes were all pierced, and that the water was rising upon the Land-scheiding, the strong dyke, within five miles of Leyden, serving to keep us from the sea.

Ah, glad news! The letter was read in the market-place of Leyden, and the city musicians were sent about the streets playing, and cannon were fired.

But the gladness passed as the days went by. Where was the flood of waters which we had believed would come to dismay the Spaniards, and to bring us the ships of our friends? Were we then deceived?

A few of the citizens of Leyden were royalists, and they taunted us with our hope of relief.

"Go up to the tower, ye beggars," cried the royalists; "go up to the tower, and tell us if ye can see the ocean coming over the dry land to your relief."

And day after day we climbed the ruined, ancient tower of Hengist, to see if the waters of the ocean were in sight.

Below we could see the lime trees, poplars, and willows that bordered the interlacing divisions of the Rhine that flowed through our city. Some of the one hundred and forty-five bridges that crossed the numerous water-courses could be seen. The city had been most beautiful. Alas, what blight had fallen upon it! Starvation was in our streets, in the elegant houses—in the spacious squares.

Many a time did I sit in the tower of Hengist, straining my eyes looking out over the wide, level country, hoping, praying, longing to see the glittering line that would tell me the ocean was coming. When would it come? Should we be alive then?

One morning Gaspar and Eliezer and I, with two other friends, known by us to be Anabaptists, climbed the artificial elevation on which, in Leyden's center, the ruined tower of Hengist stood. Gaunt skeletons that we were, we climbed still higher, gasping with the weakness of starvation, till we reached the mouldering battlements of the tower itself. We looked abroad, but the land was dry. From sheer weakness we did not descend, but remained on our lofty lookout.

All day our despairing watch was shared now and again by others, eager-eyed men and women, with emaciated, heroic faces. But the sea came not. Yet only a few days before the Estates had sent word to us : " Rather will we see our whole land and all our possessions perish in the waves, than forsake thee, Leyden. We know full well, moreover, that with Leyden all Holland must perish also."

The day wore by, and still we strained our eyes to see. The other persons who had climbed the tower had gone away, and at sunset there remained on the battlements only our little company of five Anabaptists.

The sun went down.

" Does the sea come ? " cried a company of Dutch, stopping an instant beneath the tower.

" No," we answered.

As long as possible, with eyes that grew dim and blurred through the watching, we waited. The sunlight faded. No change came on the horizon's rim. The redoubts of the enemy faded.

Afar in some street below, I heard a wild voice singing that song of the people.

CHAPTER XX

LEYDEN IS SAVED

I SHIVERED as I listened to that voice.
" '*T swaert is getrokken!*" muttered Eliezer fiercely, at my side.

"My son! my son!" cautioned Gaspar, "the
sword of vengeance is not ours, but the Lord's!
May he forgive our enemies!"

And falling on his knees, Gaspar prayed
silently.

Eliezer stood a moment. I knew the struggle
that went on within his heart. It was hard to
say, "Father, forgive them!" when the Spanish
troops hemmed us around and thirsted for our
blood. It was hard to pray and wait—yes, it was
hard to wait for God! To wait and starve!

But my boy dropped on his knees beside his
father. Our little Anabaptist group was very
still. Those of us who were not praying were
scanning yet with prayerful eyes the little of the
country visible.

Faintly the words of the singer came up from
some far distance of the streets. Eliezer shuddered, and the fingers that covered his face inter-
locked more closely.

The words of the Duke of Alva's circular,

published in all the cities of the Netherlands, after
the fall of Haarlem, mocked me with remembrance and would not leave me this night. The
pretended affection spoken of in the circular, its
lying promise, the blasphemous assumption that
Philip's will and God's were identical, all came
back to me with bitter force.

"Ye are well aware," the circular ran, "that
the King has, over and over again, manifested his
willingness to receive his children, in however
forlorn a condition the prodigals might return.
His Majesty assures you once more that your sins,
however black they may have been, shall be forgiven and forgotten in the plenitude of the royal
kindness, if you repent and return in season to his
Majesty's embrace. Notwithstanding your mani-
fold crimes, his Majesty still seeks, *like a hen calling her chickens, to gather you all under the
parental wing.* The King hereby warns you
once more, therefore, to place yourselves in his
royal hands, *and not to wait for his rage, cruelty,
and fury,* and the approach of his army.

"But if," went on the circular, "ye disregard
these offers of mercy, receiving them with closed
ears, as heretofore, then we warn you that there
is no rigor, nor cruelty, however great, which you
are not to expect by laying waste, starvation and
the sword, in such manner that nowhere shall
remain a relic of that which at present exists, but
his Majesty will strip bare and *utterly depopulate
the land,* and cause it to be inhabited *again by*

strangers; since otherwise his Majesty could not believe that the *will of God and of his Majesty* had been accomplished."

Was God's will then King Philip's? Should we all be exterminated?

The light faded entirely from the sky. Had God forgotten us? Did he, then, not care whether his creatures had religious liberty or not? We could never have it under Spain's rule! Would he leave us in the hand of Spain?

I remembered the prayers I had heard Anabaptists pray for the coming of religious freedom. I remembered the multitudes of Anabaptist martyrs of this land. So many more Anabaptists had been killed than men of other beliefs. I remembered Gaspar's saying that religious freedom would rise from Anabaptist graves. I recalled the face of the Rebaptizer strangled in the prison long ago, his eyes appealing upward to the God of freedom. I remembered the pitiful sacrifices that Anabaptists had made to help, from their scanty means, the cause of William the Silent. And now the fate of religious liberty for Holland hung on this one city of Leyden. Would God let the Spanish king conquer?

The darkness fell upon our little Anabaptist group when we went under the oaks that overgrew the center of the ruined old tower of Hengist. We had not spoken much together since we had answered the call of those who passed the foot of the tower.

But now a low sobbing broke the silence of the dark.

"Oh, God of religious liberty!" the low, agonized voice sobbed reverently. "Oh, God of liberty!"

There was no word of petition save that. The voice itself was a prayer.

There were other hushed sobs among our weak and starving little company. And then, when silence came, a voice began to pray.

"Oh, God of freedom!" prayed Gaspar, taking up the thought that the other voice had sobbed; "God of soul-liberty, thou seest our starving city! O Lord, we implore thee, may the prayers of thy Anabaptist martyrs be answered! Thine unnumbered Anabaptist martyrs, O Lord, who have suffered fire, and pit, and stake, and horrors unutterable! O Lord God of soul-liberty, Spain and the pope are thine enemies! Save Leyden! O God, save Leyden! For if Leyden falls, whence shall religious liberty ever come for this, our native land? O Lord God, thou knowest!"

And, falling prone on his face, my husband wept with all our company.

It was on the first of September, as we discovered afterward, that Admiral Boisot came to Holland from Zealand, with eight hundred savage Zealanders in his vessels. We did not know that two hundred vessels, manned with twenty-five hundred veterans, had assembled, and were coming to our relief. All we knew was that the ocean did not come, and we were starving! starving! And, if we had known what force was coming, we might also have known that the Spanish King's force was four times as great as that of those who wished to help us. And, between our friends and us were several dykes, besides villages; and the chain of sixty-two forts, as well as those villages, was held by King Philip's veteran troops. How little prospect there was that help could reach us! Yet we prayed.

And now I must tell you what we heard afterward, for being shut in the city, we could not by any manner of means know what our rescuers knew. I have told you that, before this, we had received word that the outer dykes were pierced, and that the water was rising upon the strong dyke, the "Land-scheiding," within five miles of Leyden. But the water did not rise above this dyke. The fleet of our rescuers could not therefore pass it, the Land-scheiding being still a foot and a half above water.

But the Prince of Orange had given orders that the Land-scheiding should be taken possession of. There were but a few Spaniards stationed on the dyke, and on the night of the 10th and 11th of September, the prince's orders were obeyed, and the Land-scheiding was taken without the loss of a man of William's forces.

But when day came the Spaniards saw what a mistake they had made in leaving the Land-scheiding so poorly guarded, and rushing from two villages near the dyke, King Philip's forces charged William's. There was a hot battle, but the Spaniards were defeated. Hundreds of them were killed, and under the very eyes of the enemy our rescuers cut the dyke in several places. The fleet sailed through.

But now there was a surprise. Prince William had been told by those who said they knew the country, that if the Land-scheiding once were passed, the water would flood the country as far as Leyden. But this was not so. Three-quarters of a mile further inland was another long dyke called the "Green-way," and this stood a foot above the water.

The Spanish, however, had providentially been careless about this dyke also, and Admiral Boisot took the barrier promptly, leveled it in many places, and brought his vessels over it. Now he had expected to have immediately floated into a large mere, called the Fresh-water Lake, but he found that he could reach it by only one deep canal. And now the sea failed him, for its waters had spread out over so wide a surface that no place, save the canal, was deep enough for his ships. And if he took the canal, that led to a bridge, where were many of the enemy.

He tried to force a passage, but was defeated. And now, in the shallow water, the flotilla was obliged to stay, unable to help us. The wind was easterly, and this made the sea rather sink than rise. In Leyden we were anxious over that same easterly wind. Every morning we looked at the vanes of the steeples. We climbed the towers and housetops, and looked and longed for the ocean, and yet we knew it could not appear unless the wind changed.

Oh, how often, as we watched the vanes to see if any change came; or as from the tower of Hengist I felt the easterly wind blow, I longed and prayed that the wind might shift; and I remembered the words of the psalmist: " He bringeth the wind out of his treasuries. . . He causeth his wind to blow, and the waters flow." If some " stormy wind, fulfilling his word," might but sweep from some other direction than that whence the wind now came !

For we were in dreadful straits for food. We had lived on animals we should once have shuddered to have eaten. Still a few cows, kept for their milk, remained. Some of these were killed daily, and divided into so small portions that the famishing people could hardly live on the morsels. Even the hides of the cows, chopped and boiled, were eagerly eaten. The green leaves of the trees and every living herb were gathered, and yet people starved to death. Mothers dropped dead in the streets, holding in their arms lifeless babes. And, worse than all, the plague broke out in Leyden. Hope died in our hearts.

On the eighteenth, we knew that the wind had changed. It blew a gale for three days. But we could not of course tell what this availed. We

did not know that before the second day was over
the fleet of our rescuers was again afloat.

One evening we crept to the tower of Hengist.
The last sight that I saw before climbing the
tower was a woman sitting, holding her dead
child in her lap. The woman's head drooped forward, her eyes were shut.

"Touch her not," whispered Gaspar, his gaunt
hand drawing me back; "the plague is upon
her."

Stepping aside to avoid contamination, we
dragged ourselves upward to the battlements, and
sank there.

It grew dark rapidly. The wind swept over us.

"Is it again an easterly wind?" I questioned
myself.

It did not matter. I had lost hope that our
friends would reach us while we lived. All I had
eaten that day was some green leaves.

We did not talk to one another, but sat in the
dark while the hours passed. I had closed my
eyes.

"A light! A light!" screamed Gaspar, weakly.
"A light!"

Startled, I looked and saw what brought cries
from rooftops and towers throughout the city.

"It is the village of Zoetermeer," called one
voice in the dark.

"It is Benthuyzen," disputed another voice,
thrilled with excitement.

Both were right, as we discovered afterward.

The Spanish had been stationed at each village, but some fugitives having shown our friends the way to a lower dyke, the Spaniards had been seized by a panic and had fled inwardly toward Leyden, stopping at the village of North Aa. Our friends' fleet allowed the few remaining villagers to have time enough to flee from Zoetermeer and Benthuyzen, and then those villages, together with the fortifications, were set on fire. It was this blaze that we saw at Leyden.

"Our friends are coming!" we cried to one another through the darkness, not knowing to whom we spoke save that we all were people in mighty peril. "William the Silent has not forgotten us."

After this we heard salvos of artillery, yet we could not tell the exact import of the sounds, and days passed but no fleet came. Alas! the wind had changed. It was easterly again.

Hundreds of the people of Leyden died of the plague. Yea, thousands died, and morning by morning Gaspar and Eliezer and I looked at each other, marveling that we were yet alive. For now we heard of houses where the watchmen found whole families, fathers, mothers, children dead side by side. And now, again and again, came letters from Valdez, the leader of the Spaniards, asking us to surrender and making us fair promises. But, though gradually, as the helpless days went by, we had given up hope of aid, we would not yield to our besiegers. We did not know that it was because Valdez feared that the ocean might yet liberate us, that he sent so many missives.

Yet there were some faint hearts in Leyden, and a company of them was seen by Gaspar one day near where the church of St. Pancras stood with its high two-turreted brick tower and its two ancient lime trees. The company gathered about the burgomaster, Adrian van der Werf, reproaching and threatening him.

The tall, haggard burgomaster waved his hat for silence, and cried out: " What would ye, my friends ? Why do ye murmur that we do not break our vows and surrender the city to the Spaniards ? A fate more horrible than the agony which she now endures would be ours. I tell you I have made an oath to hold the city, and may God give me strength to keep my oath."

And so did the burgomaster inspire the crowd with his courage that the people went away, famishing still, but enthusiastic, and ready to defy the enemy.

The twenty-eighth of September a dove flew into our city. Blessed little messenger ! It bore a letter from Admiral Boisot saying that in a very few days at the utmost help would come to us. The bells of Leyden rang for joy.

But Gaspar looked so gaunt and feeble that I asked myself : " Can he live a few days longer?"

And when the morrow came the vanes still pointed to the east. The water would never rise with the wind from that direction. We knew it

only too well. But we did not know that Admiral
Boisot had written to William the Silent saying
that if there did not come the fall tide and
a strong wind nothing more could be done. The
expedition must be abandoned.

It was time for the autumnal equinox. Gaspar,
used to the sea from his boyhood, had thought of
what the extraordinary tide might do if a change
of wind came.

"The God of freedom is the God of tempests
also," said he to me that night, and then he went
away alone to the tower of Hengist.

When midnight came and he had not returned,
I sent Eliezer for his father. But though Gaspar
returned with him, he could not sleep. The old
sailor spirit was alive in him, and he told me of
storms he had known in autumn equinoctial days.
When he ceased talking I knew that he prayed.
And indeed so did we all.

The next night, the last night of September,
we all were in the tower of Hengist praying. I
am certain we were praying, though we said no
word aloud for a long time. At last Gaspar spoke.

"My Editha," he said, "my Editha."

There was a silence.

"What is it, Gaspar?" I asked at last, for the
silence began to make me afraid.

He did not answer.

"Gaspar!" I cried.

I reached forward in the dark and laid my hand
on his arm.

"Gaspar !" I repeated. "Gaspar !"

Eliezer had put his arm around his father. To-gether my boy and I helped Gaspar from the tower to the humble little place in which we lived. But in all the way home my husband neither spoke nor gave any sign that he knew what we said to him. All that night and the next day he lay almost unconscious.

When night came again a storm had arisen. It became a violent gale that blew from the north-west and then tumultuously from the southwest. The equinoctial tempest for which we had prayed had come. But I had hardly noticed what went on outdoors. The longed-for tempest was as nothing to me now with Gaspar lying so. More-over I was growing too weak to reason much about the wind.

The storm increased as the night went by. I was sitting by Gaspar when I was a little startled on looking at him to see that his eyes were open. I hastily tried to give him some few morsels of meat that an Anabaptist woman had, in her great sympathy and by much sacrifice, obtained for me. I did not know from what animal the meat had come. I would not conjecture. Hunger had taught us of Leyden to be chary of questions. For myself, I knew I was starving to death.

But Gaspar put aside the food, though I begged him to eat.

"I cannot," he answered feebly. "Has the storm come, Editha ?"

The wind roared its answer outside.

"Yes," I too replied.

Gaspar closed his eyes. As I watched him, the tears rolled from beneath his shut lids.

"Leyden is safe," he whispered. "Our prayers are answered. The God of tempests is the God of freedom also."

He spoke no more, and seemed to relapse into the state of unconsciousness from which the tempest perhaps had roused him. I watched beside him all the next day. Eliezer was desperately trying to find food for us. When night came, Gaspar was still unconscious.

In the depths of that night a mysterious and dreadful sound roared through the city. I was startled. Were the Spanish upon us?

There was an extreme blackness of this night, and as I trembled I thought indefinitely that the darkness might have helped the Spaniards make an assault on Leyden. I was still wondering what the crash had been, when Gaspar's eyes opened. He looked steadfastly at me.

"My Editha," he whispered faintly; "my Editha, I am going to the land of freedom."

His face was very pale. I tried to say something. His face with the gaunt hollows in his emaciated cheeks swam before me. My head fell forward on his hand. My last conscious thought was that if the Spaniards had taken the city Gaspar and I would soon be together in the better country of which he spoke. But I knew not what had happened. Out on the southern coast of Holland the waters of the North Sea had piled themselves in great masses and had dashed furiously on the land, over the cut dykes, on over the country. The first night of the tempest the fleet of our rescuers had been lifted and sailed in the storm and darkness. There was a fierce naval battle by night, where the branches of drowned orchards and the chimney-stacks of submerged farmhouses stood above the waves. The Spanish vessels were sunk, and our rescuers' fleet came on.

Five hundred yards from our city was the fort of Zoeterwoude. In the early morning the Spaniards, seized with the general panic that I believe was sent of God upon them, they having both troops and artillery sufficient to have roughly met the light flotilla of our friends, poured out from the fortress and fled along a road that led toward the city of the Hague.

But the flood constantly deepened, and hundreds of the Spanish troops sank beneath the water. The Zealanders, moreover, sprang from their vessels to the crumbling dyke and drove the Spaniards mercilessly into the sea. Plunging into the waves, the Zealanders attacked the Spanish with boat-hooks and daggers. No one ever knew how many Spaniards fell, but hundreds must have perished. Those Spaniards who escaped fled to the Hague.

Then was the fort of Zoeterwoude set on fire, and our rescuers passed to the last fortress between them and Leyden, the fort of Lammen, only two hundred and fifty yards from our city. But this fort was filled with the enemy's soldiers and artillery, and all day Admiral Boisot stayed anchored, trying to think what to do. The fort was so very strong. It looked now, to our rescuers, as if the enterprise might all be a failure, although Leyden had almost been reached.

Inside our city the people were growing wild with excitement. Help seemed so near.

But the night came—the night of pitch blackness in which I waited so anxiously before passing into unconsciousness beside Gaspar. And oh, how anxiously those night hours went by for other folk in Leyden! Strange things happened that night of prayer and sleeplessness. In the dead of night, out from the fort of Lammen there seemed to come a long procession of lights that passed over the water. Then an awful sound crashed through the blackness. It was the mysterious noise that had startled me as I sat beside my husband. I could not guess its meaning. The truth was that the whole of the wall of our city, between the Tower of Burgundy and the Cow gate, had fallen.

"The Spaniards are upon us! The Spaniards are upon us!" cried one to another.

And truly, if the Spaniards had known their opportunity, they would have been upon us. But the falling of the town wall sent as much terror to their hearts as to ours. In the darkness, the Span-

iards thought that the desperate citizens of Leyden were coming forth to battle.

An overwhelming terror, sent upon the Spaniards from the Lord of Hosts who had fought for
us with his tempest and his tide, fell upon our
foes. Surely, as the Lord in olden time made the
host of the Syrians affrighted at no human foe,
but at the noise he caused them to hear, so that
they fled dismayed, and the siege of famished Sa-
maria ended, so did the Lord our God send panic
among the Spaniards, and they fled in the night.

When day came, Admiral Boisot, not knowing
what had come to pass, prepared to give battle to
the Spanish force in the fort of Lammen. But
the fort was very still. What did this mean?
Were the Spaniards already in Leyden, killing
the people there?

Suddenly a man was seen wading through the
deep water from the fort toward the fleet. Upon
the top of the fort a boy waved his cap.

The Spanish, with whom the admiral had expected to have a hard and perhaps unsuccessful
battle, had fled. Valdez, the Spanish commander,
had also fled from his headquarters at Leyderdorp,
within a mile of the city of Leyden. At the very
moment when the city wall fell, leaving ample
way for our foes to enter Leyden, they trembled
and ran away.

And so triumphantly the fleet of our rescuers
swept past the last fort and into Leyden. Our city
was saved.

Every human being in Leyden, able to stand, rushed to greet the coming fleet. Bread! Bread! Bread! It was thrown from every vessel. The crowd caught the blessed gift. Bread! Bread! And when the admiral stepped on shore, a solemn procession was formed; the magistrates, the citizens, the burgher guards, the sailors, the women, the children, all poured into the church and sent up a prayer of thanksgiving to God. Thousands of voices raised a song of thanksgiving, but the hymn broke, and the great audience sobbed and wept. The people were saved.

But Gaspar and I knew nothing of it all. Relief came almost too late for us both. Eliezer had found us both unconscious, and frantic with grief had hastily summoned two or three friends who did what they could. It was starvation that affected us, and not the plague, as Eliezer had feared.

Within the next few hours, as I have said, the fleet entered Leyden, and food could be obtained.

I can never forget my feelings the next day when I regained consciousness, and without opening my eyes, thought "I am alive! I am alive, and Gaspar is dead."

How could I live without him? Yet I must live for Eliezer's sake.

"Take this," a quiet voice commanded me.

I feebly opened my eyes. A woman was trying to make me take a spoonful of something warm and nourishing. And there beyond her, sat Gaspar—gaunt, haggard, but alive, *alive!*

V

Eliezer was giving his father a little broth.

I swallowed what the woman gave me. I shut my eyes and tried to think. We were alive. It was an overwhelming thought at first.

"The Spaniards will kill us," I said to myself. Then I began to wonder where the broth came from.

"She is better," I heard the woman's voice say.

And then my dear boy, Eliezer, dropped on his knees beside me, and cried in my ear: "Mother! Mother! You are going to live! We all are! Leyden is safe! The Spaniards are all gone! The ships have come!"

Slowly I took into my mind what it was that he said. His voice had sounded dimly in my ears, as Gaspar's voice sounded years before when I was so nearly buried alive, and he cried to me as he strove to help me, "Editha, Editha, live a little longer!"

By afternoon, such was the strength that food put into me, I was quite conscious, though weak as I lay listening to the wind. It blew a tempest.

Eliezer came in with an awestruck look on his thin face.

"Mother," he said,—and his tone was thrilled with a reverent fear, as if he had looked on the work of the Almighty,—"mother, the Lord is rolling back the waters to the ocean. The wind is northeast. Oh, mother, if this wind had come a day or two ago, the fleet could never have reached us to help us."

The wind did blow, as my son said. In a few days the land near Leyden was bare again, and the people began to rebuild the cut dykes. Never did I feel more truly that the hand of the Lord had wrought for us, the hand of that God who divided the Red Sea and the Jordan for his people.

"Do you not remember," Gaspar reminded me, "what William, Prince of Orange, wrote after Haarlem was laid desolate by our enemies? He said : ' Before I ever took up the cause of the oppressed Christians in these provinces, I had entered into a close alliance with the King of kings. The God of armies will raise up armies for us to do battle with our enemies and his own.' Has not God done as the prince said? The armies of the waves and the winds have fought for us."

Four years before this, when the sea rose on the whole Netherland coast from Flanders to Friesland, when dykes broke and when so many persons were drowned, the Spaniards had loudly cried that the vengeance of heaven had descended upon the abode of heretics. What would the Spaniards say now when the waves had been our friends?

I shuddered when I remembered that nine years ago Philip II. had suggested, and orders had been sent forth, that heretics should be executed at midnight in their dungeons by binding their heads between their knees, and then slowly suffocating the victims in tubs of water. Many of Philip's soldiers lay drowned to-day. Had God sent his waters in vengeance upon them.

CHAPTER XXI

AFTER THE SIEGE

A COMPANY of us went forth from Leyden to look at the broken dykes. We walked afar beside the heaps where people already worked, repairing the bulwarks. The ground was yet damp and we went farther than we meant, for it seemed wonderful to be able to go forth from our city where we had been shut so long.

Together, a woman and I climbed a portion of the dyke yet whole. I reached the top first, and looking over, cried aloud.

"What see you?" asked the woman who came after me.

I pointed.

Below us, where we could plainly view their faces, lay the bodies of several Spanish soldiers where they had fallen beneath the boathooks of the Zealanders. The woman with me shrieked aloud, as I had, and turning, we both fled back toward the ruined fort of Zoeterwoude. Yet, as I fled, I knew that I remembered one of those Spanish faces. I should always remember it. I had seen it in my dreams often as I lived again that dreadful hour of the past.

It was the face of that Spanish soldier who,

In Editha's Days   Page 324

Walking on the Dyke

years before, tore my baby Hendrick from my arms and threw him into the canal. Those Spanish lips that were mute now had laughed at my agony. That voice that nevermore would mock at his victims had sneered: "Anabaptists, I can baptize a child! See me play the priest!"

Once more I could hear my child's last cry; I could hear the splash, far out in the canal; I could see that mother struggle to break through the soldiers; I could see that father grapple with the men who held him.

The woman running beside me, now grasped my hand and drew me up to the ruins of the fort of Zoeterwoude.

"How pale you are," she said. "Were you so frightened? I am glad they are dead, those Spanish."

And in a whisper, for she herself was trembling and could hardly have sung, she broke forth into that song of the people, so awful to me: "'*T swaert is getrokken*.'"

I rushed away from her. I could not bear to hear the words. I was glad she was not an Anabaptist, for one of our faith—yes, one of any faith—should have forgiveness for one's enemies. And yet—was I glad to have seen that Spanish soldier lying there?

Oh, that long hour that I walked those broken dykes, wrestling with my innermost soul! Did I forgive this enemy of mine, this man who, even if he were dead, had done me the most cruel

wrong of my life? Was I glad—could a Christian heart be *glad* to see one's enemy lying torn
and pierced with the boathook, face and clenched
hands showing the agony in which he had died?

"It is the vengeance of the Lord!" I shuddered as I walked. "It is the vengeance of the
Lord!"

I had thought that I had fought this heart-
battle years before. I had struggled often to pray
for this Spanish soldier, that his awful sin toward
me and mine might be forgiven him. I *had*
prayed. I had thought I had obtained grace of
God to forgive even this man. But in that hour
alone upon the broken dykes I fought the battle
over again. The Spanish soldier's face had
brought back to me the fierce hatred that had
often knocked at my soul's door when I remembered how I had been robbed of my boy.

"Lord," I cried, lifting my hands toward the
grayness of the heavens as I stood alone among the
ruins of the dykes, "help me to forgive! Help
me to forgive as I would be forgiven!"

When peace came to me, I went back to the
city; nor did I ever tell my husband or my son
of what I had seen. I would not rouse again in
their hearts the battle that had raged in mine.
But I write it here that I saw the dead Spanish
soldier who had so cruelly used me and mine.
When my son Eliezer reads this chronicle he will
see what I have said of that of which I could
never bring myself to speak either to him or to

his father. For I can never now think of the Spanish soldier's mocking, laughing face, but I also see that same face, white and marred and ghastly, an awful thing looking up from the spot where he had fallen when God summoned his soul to eternity.

Let me speak of other matters. No one must think that because the Spanish army was defeated at Leyden therefore King Philip relinquished his efforts and left the Netherlands at peace. Religious and civil liberty did not come so easily.

Some of our friends thought of going to England, where Queen Mary was long since dead and where Queen Elizabeth had enforced severe laws against the Catholics. But Gaspar and I mistrusted the English queen, and we felt more than glad the next year that we had not attempted once again to reach my native land.

1575
A.D.

For there came a woman to the little town where Gaspar and Eliezer and I were living in a boat, and as she passed us she seemed so weary that I spoke to her, and she rested a little on our boat. And often thereafter, since she had found that we were Anabaptists, she would stop to speak a word on her way as she went to or from the little town.

Once I ventured to ask her, since she always was sad of countenance, if she was in trouble.

"God knows the troubles of his Anabaptists," she answered, bursting into tears.

She told me her sad story. She had long been an Anabaptist, and had suffered much from the devastations of the Duke of Alva in Flanders. With a number of other Anabaptists, she had fled to Protestant England, thinking that there would be religious freedom in that country. But they discovered that the spirit of toleration was not in England.

"It was last Easter time," she told me, "that about thirty of us Anabaptists met for worship in an upper room near the Aldgate in London. We held our meeting very quietly, but some of the neighbors discovered it, and a constable and two officers came to us, and addressed us as devils. The constable had twenty-seven names taken down, and at last we were conducted to jail. Two escaped on the way.

"The third day we were released, but afterward we were summoned to appear before the court in St. Paul's, and commanded to recant. We were spoken to kindly at first, but afterward we were told that if we did not recant we should be banished or killed.

"We were asked various questions, one being whether infants should not be baptized. We answered that we could not understand matters so, for we read nothing of it in the Scriptures. After answering these questions, we were told by the bishop that our misdeeds were very gross, and that we could not inherit the kingdom of God.

"When we were in prison, after this examination, five of our number were persuaded to abjure, taking oath henceforth to utterly abandon and forsake 'all and every Anabaptistical error.'

"A few days afterwards, in the court room of St. Paul's Church, the rest of us were all condemned to death. We women were bound hand to hand, and taken with one of the brethren, the youngest, to Newgate prison. The other men were taken back to the bishop's prison.

"We women were kept in suspense five or six days, supposing every day that we would be burnt, for people came every day to threaten us, and tell us that we should be put to death if we did not abjure. One evening about ten o'clock, the bailiff came with a servant into the prison to take an inventory of all our property, telling us that we must prepare for death the next day. But when we all kept steadfast and did not show ourselves afraid, the bailiff told us the truth. He said that the queen would be gracious to us, and merely banish us from the country, and that the young man should be whipped behind a cart.

"So, five or six days afterward, we fourteen women were taken from the prison to the ship that was to bear us away from England. The young brother was whipped behind a cart till he came to the place where we took ship. Some of us left our husbands, some our fathers, behind us in the hands of the persecutors, and I do not know even to this day, what was done with my poor husband."

And here the woman who spoke with me wept very bitterly.

Nor did she know her husband's lot, for much time ofter this. Alas, poor man! When we did hear, the news was sad enough for his wife. There had been five of these Anabaptist men left behind. They were sentenced to death and taken to New-gate, where they were heavily ironed and put into a deep and dreadful den where, after eight days, the poor husband of the woman who told me of her own banishment died "of wretchedness and a load of chains." But his dying testimony filled the other Anabaptists with joy.

A petition and a confession of the faith of the four remaining Anabaptists were presented to Queen Elizabeth, but she did not believe in religious freedom and would have no mercy. Even when John Foxe, whom Queen Elizabeth used to call "my father Foxe," wrote a letter pleading with the queen, she refused to change her mind. Those Anabaptists must die.

Queen Elizabeth granted them a month yet of life, but two of the imprisoned Anabaptists were told, early in July, that they must die. The two men who suffered at this time were Jan Peters, who had hoped to be more safe in England than in the Low Countries, and Hendrick Terwoort, who had been married only about eight or ten weeks before he was put in prison.

Jan Peters, whose first wife had, some years before, been burned for her religion at Ghent, in

Flanders, had entreated to be allowed to leave England with his second wife and his children. But the bishop would not allow it. And so the 22d of July, the two Anabaptists were tied to one stake at Smithfield.

An English preacher stood by and cried out, "These men believe not on God."

But Jan Peters said : "We believe in one God, one Heavenly Father almighty, and in Jesus Christ his Son."

And so, refusing to abjure their faith, although a last chance of doing so was offered to them while bound to the stake, the two Anabaptists bravely died.

Could we dare go back to an England where such things were done to Anabaptists, and where the queen herself had commanded all holding "such heretical opinions as Anabaptists do hold," to depart from her realm?

In the next year the Ghent Pacification was brought about in the Low Countries. By this the Inquisition was agreed to be forever abolished. Our whole nation, Catholics and Reformers, agreed to unite to expel the foreign soldiers. Fifteen provinces were Catholic, but in them it was agreed that there was to be no prohibition of private Reformed worship. It was recognized as a fact that the "new religion" was to be the established creed of Holland and Zealand. This Pacification was the work of William the Silent, and was the agreement of the Catholics and the Protestants of

1576
A.D.

the Netherlands, though not the agreement of Philip, the Spanish king, by any means.

His soldiers, this very year, most dreadfully massacred the people of Antwerp. This was one of the most terrible things ever done in the Netherlands, and for many long years, as I well remember, it was called, " The Spanish Fury."

It will be seen that the Ghent Pacification meant peace and liberty for the Catholics and the Reformed, if the promises were kept. But what did it mean for us Anabaptists? Were we to have freedom? We who had believed in the idea and suffered most for it?

Don John of Austria came to the Low Countries in that year, and the Pacification of Ghent was rather weakened than otherwise.

It seemed to be impossible for William of Orange to teach his nearest friends that toleration and religious freedom are good things. It was apparently impossible for even Christian people to believe that those who thought differently should not be treated with force to make them change their religious convictions. The Reformed thought William did very wrong not to persecute the Catholics. And how terrible a thing it was that William would not exclude the Anabaptists of Holland from the rights of citizenship! William's intimate counselor, Saint Aldegonde, an accomplished man, was in despair because the prince would not exclude the Anabaptists.

"The affair of the Anabaptists," wrote Saint

Aldegonde, "has been renewed. The prince objects to exclude them from citizenship. He answered me sharply that their yea was equal to our oath, and that we should not press the matter, unless we were *willing to confess that it was just for the Papists to compel us* to a divine service which was against our conscience."

It seems strange to an Anabaptist that so intelligent and accomplished a Protestant as Saint Aldegonde could not see how true and forcible were William's words. And yet Saint Aldegonde was vexed that he could not see the Anabaptists excluded from citizenship.

"I don't see how we can accomplish our wish in this matter," wrote Saint Aldegonde. "The prince has uttered reproaches to me that our clergy are striving to obtain a mastery over consciences. He praised lately the saying of a monk who was not long ago here, that our pot had not gone to the fire so often as that of our antagonists, but that when the time came it would be black enough. In short, the prince fears that after a few centuries the clerical tyranny on both sides will stand in this respect on the same footing."

It truly seemed as if William the Silent were right. The Protestants—not the Anabaptists, but the Reformed—acted as if they indeed had a "mastery over consciences" of other people. Many were the Reformed who would have liked to suppress Catholicism by the same enginery that the Catholics had formerly used. We should have had a Protestant Inquisition in the Netherlands if some Reformers had had their way. No wonder William charged them not to press the matter of Anabaptist exclusion, unless willing to confess that it had been just for the Papists to tyrannize over men's consciences.

Such turning of the tables as that, of course, would not be agreed to by any of William's friends, yet they thought it right to persecute us Anabaptists. It was wrong for the Catholics to persecute the Reformed, and yet, if the Reformed could in turn have persecuted the Catholics, many would have done it. It was wrong for the Catholics to persecute the Reformed, and yet if the Reformed could make the lives of Anabaptists miserable, many believed in doing it. It seemed strange that people but lately delivered themselves from persecution should be so ready to turn persecutors, and that in matters of conscience.

Gaspar and Eliezer and I dwell now in Middelburg, on the island of Walcheren, in Zealand. 1579 Thither have we journeyed, thinking to be A.D. more safe. But we have found here that Anabaptists must expect persecution. The magistrates have not protected us, but Anabaptist shops have been shut, and we have not been allowed to earn our living, because of our religious belief. The Protestants are much of the same mind as Prince William's counselor, Saint Aldegonde, who wrote impatiently of the prince's tolerance toward us.

But tidings of the woeful plight of the Anabaptists of Middelburg went to Prince William's ears last year.   1578 A.D.

And again did William of Orange come to our aid, reminding the magistrates of Middelburg that the Anabaptists were always perfectly willing to bear their part in all the common burdens; that the word of the Anabaptists was as good as their bond; and that, in regard to military service, though the principles of the Anabaptists forbade them to bear arms, yet these people had always been ready to provide and pay for substitutes.

"We declare to you therefore," said William the Silent to the magistrates, "that you have no right to trouble yourselves with any man's conscience, so long as nothing is done to cause private harm or public scandal. We therefore expressly ordain that you desist from molesting these Baptists, from offering hindrance to their handicraft and daily trade, by which they can earn bread for their wives and children, and that you permit them henceforth to open their shops and do their work, according to the custom of former days. Beware, therefore, of disobedience and of resistance to the ordinance which we now establish."

Will the magistrates obey? If William the Silent should die, would there be any toleration for us Anabaptists? I think not. And yet we wait, and suffer, and hope, and pray that religious freedom may come to this land. And by word and example we do strive to teach men religious toleration.

And now, if any one should ask me, "What have you Anabaptists done to bring to pass your vision of religious freedom for all men?" I would answer: "We have given of our hearts' blood for freedom of conscience; we have given those dearest on earth to die by stake, by strangulation, by living burial, because neither we nor they would agree to have our consciences domineered over by priest or pope; we have wept tears of blood and agony; we have prayed to our God night and day; we have given our scanty money to freedom's cause. We have not fought for freedom of conscience, many of us, because many of us have believed war to be wrong. Our Master said: 'If my kingdom were of this world, then would my servants fight, . . but now is my kingdom not from hence.' We have suffered and we have appealed to the God who has promised to hear his people's cries. He will deliver."

What have we done for religious freedom? Ask those whom the priests of Rome have murdered. Ask the unnumbered Anabaptist dead. Oh, thou foul and bloody church of Rome, binding men's souls in fetters of spiritual death, tremble, for our God has heard the poor Anabaptists who cried out in agony! There will yet come a day when neither priest nor emperor shall be able to keep religious freedom from the people of the earth.

CHAPTER XXII

AFTER YEARS

I, PHILIP BLOUNT, am the English 1688
great-great-grandson of that Editha who A.D.
wrote of the trials of the Anabaptists in her time.
One day recently I took from an old desk in our
house the treasured, faded, yellow pages of
Editha's chronicle, and showed them to my sweetheart, Rose Spencer.

For I thought, and rightly, that Rose being a
Baptist, as I am also, and each of my forefathers
has been, back to the days of Editha, would be
pleased to read with me what my great-great-
grandmother endured for the faith's sake. And
especially was Rose glad to read the pages now,
for this year is a great year with us all as an English religious people, inasmuch that this year, for
the first time in the history of England, we are
legally tolerated, and are allowed to bear the name
of " Baptists."

I read the thin pages to Rose myself, and she
listened to the tale, and when I had finished she
looked at me, and the tears ran down her cheeks
as she said : " Philip, when I think how those
old-time Baptists suffered and died, struggling to
secure religious liberty, I feel unworthy to call

myself a Baptist. For what have I ever suffered compared with such people? It seems as if some of them ought to be alive this year to hail our victory, and to rejoice to be called Baptists, and be glad to see religious liberty in England. I can rejoice, and I do, but what is my rejoicing compared with the joy that some of those old martyrs would have had to see this day?"

But I answered my Rose: "Peace, sweetheart. Perhaps they also rejoice in heaven. And I believe that if you had lived in the days of old there would have been no braver Anabaptist than Rose Spencer."

And then we fell to talking with a kind of rightful pride of how much the Baptists have done in the past toward obtaining religious freedom, not only for themselves but for others. I told Rose some things that I think she did not know before, for I said to her that if it had not been for the help that the poor, almost starving Anabaptists gave to William, Prince of Orange, when he struggled to free the Low Countries from the power of Spain, I knew not whether William would have succeeded or not. And woe to the Low Countries if he had not succeeded! Woe to them if Roman Catholic Spain still held her grasp upon them! What would have become of the Low Countries, and of the mighty influence that they have exerted for human freedom throughout the world, if William had *not* been successful?

"And yet," I told Rose, "who can tell how much of his success was due to the Baptists? For at a time when William's affairs were at the worst; when his friends had failed him; when his money was gone, and he was almost in despair, he appealed to the Baptists, and they came to his help. Once on the outskirts of Holland there was a refugee congregation, from which a poor Anabaptist preacher collected a small sum of money, and at the risk of his life brought the money to the camp of Prince William. The Anabaptist preacher told William that the money came from the people, whose will was better than the gift, and who never would want to be repaid, except by kindness when reform should triumph in the Low Countries. And the prince signed a receipt for that money, and said that he was much touched by such sympathy. Other contributions of money came from starving and persecuted church communities, and such poor exiles gave in proportion far more toward establishing civil and religious liberty than the wealthy merchants and nobles gave."

"And Prince William did not forget it after he became a conqueror," added Rose, still fingering the pages of my great-great-grandmother's tale.

"No, he did not," I returned. "Prince William was not the man to forget. In 1577, as grandmother Editha says, when the Reformed asked that the Baptists should not be allowed to be **citizens**, because they *were* Baptists, William answered the unjust request indignantly, and said that the 'yea' of the Baptists was equal to the oath of the Reformed."

Rose smiled.

"I am glad," she answered me. "It is something that a conqueror like William the Silent should appreciate the Baptists and give such testimony concerning them."

"And the next year he rebuked the magistrates of Middelburg for persecuting the Baptists, and William praised the Baptists for being so peaceable," I added. "But oh, if any people contributed to the coming of religious freedom in the Low Countries it was the Baptists! For in the long lists of the martyrs there for half a century, ten times as many Baptists suffered as Reformed persons."

"But," Rose questioned me, her sweet lips quivering, "did the Baptists do any more for the Low Countries than for England? Think, think how our brethren have struggled here for religious liberty! Think how many have died!"

Tears filled her eyes, and I knew that she remembered the day three years before this, October 23, 1685, when she had stood at Tyburn, near London, and had seen her mother's cousin, a poor Anabaptist woman named Elizabeth Gaunt, burnt to death. The woman was a very good, kind person, who spent a great part of her time visiting the jails and looking after the poor, and when she was burnt to death she so behaved herself that all the spectators wept. And my Rose could never afterward speak of Elizabeth Gaunt without tears. For it was through the basest ingratitude and treachery that Elizabeth Gaunt, the Anabaptist, suffered death. But her judge was the infamous Jeffreys, and what else could be expected of that bloody man? And to Rose, the one burning she had witnessed was but an index of the cruelty with which the Baptists of past years in England had been treated. No wonder she wished they might have lived till now to see the day of religious freedom for which they struggled.

"Think of the days when the Baptists of Bickenhall used to meet in the woods and other places of hiding," went on Rose. "Have the English Baptists no history of which we may be proud? When Cromwell rose against that persecuting tyrant, Charles I., and became Lord Protector of the Commonwealth, did not the Baptists help in that struggle? The Baptists were not found cowards then, even if Oliver Cromwell, after he came to power, did discharge all the principal officers in his army because, among other reasons, they were Anabaptists. A grateful thing that was for Oliver Cromwell to do!"

I smiled, for a Baptist in this year of our rejoicing can afford to smile at past ills. But Rose was too much in earnest to smile.

"My father has told me of the pamphlet that a well-wisher to the Anabaptists wrote at that time to Oliver Cromwell, putting some questions to his conscience," continued she. "And it would seem there were so many Anabaptists then, for the pamphlet asked if they had not filled Cromwell's towns and cities and castles and navies and armies? I wonder if Cromwell, when he was a lad, ever heard of that treatise that Mr. Helwise and his Anabaptist church of London published, in which it was written that every man hath a right to judge for himself in matters of religion, and that to persecute any one on that account is illegal and anti-Christian?"

"Cromwell was but a lad in college then," I answered. "Perhaps he did not so much care what Mr. Helwise and his church believed. But Cromwell may well have heard of the book called 'The Bloody Tenet,' and the other called 'The Compassionate Samaritan,' that said that persecution in cases of conscience was guilty of all the blood of the souls crying for vengeance under the altar. That was the time, you know, when Dr. Featly wanted that the Baptists should be *utterly exterminated* and banished out of England! And this was because the Baptists believed in religious liberty! Almost no other people in England besides the Baptists believed in liberty of conscience then."

As Rose turned over the pages of the old writing that lay in her lap, I bethought me of what other petitions Baptists had written, and of one address in particular, that speaking against using force, said: "Why, therefore, the Christian religion should be built and supported by violence, when the foundation was laid and the work carried on during all the apostles' days and some hundred years after by a quite contrary means, is a question would be resolved by those whose strongest arguments for the support of their religion is, *Take him, jailer.*"

Verily, the old Baptists waxed sarcastic! But Rose spoke.

" The old Baptist Confession of Faith, published forty years ago, shows how ready the Baptists were then to do to every man as the Baptists themselves would wish to be done by," she reminded me. " *We* were ready to grant religious freedom to every one. I believe that Baptists always have been ready to do that."

" Baptists were 'no way dangerous or troublesome to human society,'" laughed I, remembering the statement of the confession; " they were ready to give to the needy, 'both friend and enemy.'" We remembered various things that the Baptists had published.

"There was a translation from a Dutch piece printed seventy years ago in England, in 1618," Rose continued. " It was a treatise concerning baptism."

"And much I would give to see that same old treatise now," I answered. " People say it was the first that was published in English against the baptism of infants."

" No wonder the Baptists wanted to publish

something," rejoined Rose ; "it was only two
years afterward that they presented their suppli-
cation to King James, telling of their miseries.
Their goods had been seized, and Baptists then
were spoken against from the pulpits, and men
were kept in prison so long that many of them
died, leaving widows and children."

"I remember," I added, "that at one time it
was proposed that the Baptists be treated in England in some such severe way as they were by the
senate of Zurich. That condemned Anabaptists
to death, you know, and some were tied back to
back and thrown into the sea. England has done
as evil things as that to Baptists."

"England classed Baptists with the Papists,
once, in treatment," averred Rose, a stern look
coming into her eyes. "A Baptist to be counted
as a Romanist ! And there was no toleration for
either of us."

"Be not wroth, dear heart," I admonished her,
smiling, though I remembered Baptist wrongs
that brought indignation to my own soul, and
tears to my eyes. "Remember that there were
Christians, even among those persons who mis-
understood and ill-treated the Baptists ! Remember that even Dr. Featley, who wrote of the
Baptists, and was hardly able to dip his pen in
anything but gall when he wrote, yet when he had
read the Confession of Faith published by forty-
seven Baptist congregations in the country and
the seven congregations of London, acknowledged

that they were neither heretics not schismatics, but
tender-hearted Christians, upon whom, through
false suggestions, the hand of authority had fallen
heavily.''

"But he might have been more tolerant," suggested Rose. "The Baptists are, and have ever
been, willing to tolerate those of other beliefs."

"Yes," I agreed, "and we have written out
plainly our arguments about baptism that other
men might calmly read and study the matter.
Even if we had been powerful enough I do not
think we would have tried with the sword to force
our religious belief on any one.''

"It is contrary to the spirit of Christianity to
do that," stated Rose. "The Baptists urged years
ago in their appeal to the king and Parliament that
liberty 'ought to be given to all such as disturb
not the civil peace, though of different persuasions
in religious matters.'"

"And I believe," I answered, "that the Baptists, through their appeals for religious liberty for
all men, have done grander work than yet is supposed. If the day of full freedom ever comes to
all on earth, I believe that the Baptists will be the
ones to bring it, under God's providence."

Rose looked thoughtful.

"It has cost much for some to be Baptists," she
declared. "I remember hearing of a minister
who denied the baptism of infants, and he was
kept eleven months in prison."

"Ah," I replied, "remember that other poor

Baptist in Gloucestershire, the minister at Rencome, who with his wife and family was penned into an upper room of his house, and was so harassed night and day with the violence of the assailants and the noise of the hautboys that he died in the place."

"In Gloucestershire!" exclaimed Rose. "Yes, it was there that the Baptists felt suffering. My father has told me how the cavaliers would ride about with swords and pistols, ransacking the houses of the Baptists and abusing their families."

"But think of Lincolnshire," I reminded her. "When the Baptists there made their petition to King Charles II., it was signed by thirty-five Baptists in behalf of many others in Lincolnshire. It was said in the petition that not only were their meetings for religious worship interrupted, but the Baptists were abused in the streets, and were not at peace even in their own houses. For if the Baptists were heard praying to God in their families, their enemies would sound horns and beat against the doors, and make threats of hanging. And many of the Baptists were indicted at the sessions for not attending on the preaching of the Episcopal clergy."

"And think a little before that," rejoined Rose, "how the Baptists baptized men and women during the twilight in rivulets and in some arms of the Thames, and how the Baptist doctrine spread through England."

There was a little pause.

"Even our enemies have had to acknowledge the Baptists to be good people," added Rose.

"Yes," I answered, absently, for I was thinking of Henry Denne, him who was ordained by the bishop of St. David's, and who held the living of Pyrton, in Hertfordshire, for ten years. He was arrested in Cambridgeshire by the committee of that county, in 1644, and was sent to jail for preaching against infant baptism, and for baptizing those who had received no other than infant baptism. After being in jail some time, he was sent up to London, his case, through the intercession of some friends, having been referred to a committee of Parliament. He was released after hearing, but two years afterward was arrested again in Lincolnshire, being taken on Sunday, and kept to prevent his preaching. He was charged with having baptized, but there was only one witness against him, and the minister refused to be his own accuser. The baptizing had been done at night, showing how severe the persecution of Baptists was at that time. I recalled the name of another minister, a Mr. Coppe, who was sent to Coventry jail about the same time for "rebaptizing."

And yet this was far from being the worst that Baptists had suffered, whether in England or elsewhere. How they had striven for the civil and religious liberty of the countries dwelt in! What had *not* Baptists done for religious liberty in England? What had they not done in other countries?

I looked at Rose and thought how many faces, fair once almost as hers, had vanished into Baptist martyr graves; how many hands, dear perhaps as those that now softly touched the pages of my great-great-grandmother's writing, had shriveled in the fires lit to burn Baptists; how many precious heads, beloved as the golden one beside me, had sunk beneath the water, drowned by the enemies of Baptists.

Rose looked up with a little shiver.

"I bethink me," she said, with a smile, "how terrified I was once at the tale my grandmother told me when I was a child. It was of that Baptist, Robert Shalder, who suffered much in imprisonment, and who afterward died and was buried among his ancestors in Croft, of Lincolnshire. The deluded people there hated the Baptists so, that on the very day when he was buried, the grave was opened, Robert Shalder's body was taken out and dragged on a sledge back to his own gate and left there. I remember the horrified feeling I had as I thought how startling that dead Baptist must have been, lying stiff and cold in his grave clothes at his own gate! And, Philip, that happened only twenty-two years ago."

While she was speaking, I remembered a tale that startled me also when a boy. It was concerning a Baptist minister, Mr. Benjamin Keach, and it happened about 1661 or 1664.

"He was conducting a service," I told Rose, "and troopers came, swearing: 'We will kill the preacher! We will kill the preacher!' They seized him in the midst of his service. 'We will trample him to death with our horses!' cried four of the troopers. They bound the minister, laid him on the ground, and were going to spur all their four horses upon him to trample him to death! But then their officer, seeing what was intended, rode up and kept the four men from doing their murderous deed. Yet the minister was tied behind one of the troopers, across a horse, and carried to jail, where he suffered great hardships for some time before he was released. I used to imagine the scene when I was a little lad, and think how the minister must have felt, lying there with the four horses ready to trample him to death. And I would imagine myself there, rushing in to hold back the horses."

Rose smiled.

"You would have taken the part of the Baptists even then," she answered. "One would know you were Editha's great-great-grandson."

Her finger rested on a page of Editha's writing, but her thoughts were elsewhere.

"I hope," she went on, "that the Baptists of the Colonies may never have to pass through what English Baptists have endured."

She flushed slightly as she spoke. We had often talked of a plan of ours, which was to go after our marriage across the sea to the Colonies of New England, and there in the town called Providence, founded half a century ago by the banished Baptist, Roger Williams, find a home where we trusted religious persecution would never come.

"Ah," I returned, eagerly, "how grand a country might not that new world become, if only the principle for which Baptists have striven so long might have free course there—the principle of religious liberty. God grant it may. If the Colonies become a country of religious freedom, I know right well that the hand of the Baptists will have brought it about."

"Under God," added Rose, reverently.

"Under God," I repeated, softly.

"And may religious freedom come fully to England also," wished Rose. "To this England where Baptists have prayed, and fought, and suffered, and written, and plead for the religious freedom of all. How much have Baptists had to do with bringing about such freedom as England now has."

Rose looked at the pages of writing before her.

"See, Philip," she said, as she pointed to the words, and I read them once again, those prophetic words of a hunted Anabaptist, hiding in a fagot pile :

"'Editha,' cried my father, his whispering eager with excitement, 'the Anabaptists have had a glorious history in the past. They will have a glorious history in the future. Oh, my child, shall not you and I be worthy of that history? Shall we not do our part in the struggle for reli gious freedom? It will come some day, Editha, this freedom we Anabaptists want for all men. Then no man will have to hide in a fagot pile because he reads the New Testament and believes that none but those who have repented and believed should be baptized. Then every man shall be at liberty to worship God as he thinks right. Editha, I *know* the day of freedom will come, and I am proud to think what part the sacrifice of Anabaptist suffering and toil, yea the sacrifice of Anabaptist lives themselves, will have in bringing freedom to the world.'"

Rose turned to me and smiled tearfully.

"The vision for which that Baptist gave his life is coming true," she murmured.

And I answered her: "The morning of the day of freedom has come. God has granted to the Baptists grace and wisdom to plead with men for general religious freedom; to suffer banishment, and forfeiture of goods, and imprisonment for such freedom; to strive, and agonize, and die for such freedom. May God be praised! The prayers of the Baptists are being answered. The blood of their martyrs has not been spilled in vain. The day of general religious freedom is at hand. We see the glory of its dawn."

THE END

SAVED THROUGH A
TELEPHONE CONVERSATION

It really is great to know that when you die, you will go to Heaven. Before December 26, 1974, I didn't have the security of knowing this. I've always traveled a lot and at times I would think about what would happen to me if my car were to run off the road and crash and I were to die. I didn't want to think of death so I would start thinking about something else. On December 26, 1974 at 7:00 PM I accepted Jesus Christ as my personal Savior. I no longer fear death but instead I'm looking forward to spending eternity with Jesus in Heaven and also with my brother, who died on July 4, 1978, and my six-year old son, whom the Lord took in January, 1976.

I was reared on a small farm in central Mississippi and regularly attended the Baptist church a half mile away. I hardly ever missed a service, not because I enjoyed going, but because my mom and dad went and they made me go.

At the age of sixteen during a local revival and upon the insistence of my pastor and Mother, I joined the church and was baptized. Like so many people that are baptized today, I went down a dry sinner and came up a wet sinner because nobody had taken the Bible and showed me how I must repent of my sins and ask Jesus Christ to come into my heart and save me. After starting college, I rarely attended church, except when I went home and that was only to please my mother. After a year and a half of college, I entered military service and during basic training became a chapel guide in my squadron. I volunteered to do this because I felt I was religious enough and I also thought I might evade extra duty. While in Vietnam I went to church a few times, only because I felt I needed some religion to ease my conscience. About the only time I called on the Lord was when I was in trouble. Nobody had ever really witnessed to me about Heaven and Hell and although I had a small desire deep down inside to live a clean moral life, I was more interested in living a worldly life or as a beer advertiser calls it, "the good life."

After my discharge from the service, I reentered college. A year later my first marriage failed and I was free to join a fraternity and seek the pleasures of the social world. I had an apartment, sports car, friends, parties and all that goes with that life, including the emptiness. At this time my brother, Gary, was going to a Christian school in Indiana called Hyles-Anderson College. Every time he came home he would talk to me about being saved but I told him I was saved and that he should live his life and I would live mine. We were both home in Mississippi for the holidays in December, 1974 and I tried to avoid him because I knew what he was going to talk about. He finally persuaded me to listen to a tape by Evangelist J. Harold Smith called "God's Three Deadlines". I was getting convicted from listening to that tape and hoping something would happen to it and sure enough, it quit playing. "Well", I thought to myself, "that takes care of that . . ." But my brother didn't give up. He got on the phone and called a friend of his from Hammond, Indiana, who is now an evangelist and teacher named Johnny Pope. We talked for a few minutes and he asked me, "Larry, if you were to die this very minute do you know that you would go to Heaven.?" I said "Well, I hope so but I really don't know for sure." He said that the Bible tells us that we can know for sure. He read me several verses from the book of Romans which made me realize that everyone is a sinner (Rom. 3:23), that the penalty for sin is death (Rom. 6:23), that Christ has already paid the penalty (Rom. 5:8), and that it is necessary to accept what Christ has done for us as one would accept a gift

(Rom. 10:13). He then said, "Larry, wouldn't you like to be saved tonight?" I thought about it for a few seconds and I knew I really hadn't been happy with my past life so I said okay. We bowed our heads and he prayed and I prayed and trusted Jesus Christ as my Savior. I didn't have an emotional experience and I really didn't feel any different but I knew I had made a commitment to the Lord, and the Bible says we are saved by grace, through faith in Christ, not by feelings. (Eph. 2:8,9).

Brother Pope told me to be sure to tell people that I got saved. Since mother had been crying and praying for me, I was glad to let her know that I had accepted the Lord, but she didn't think I meant it. I went back to where I was going to school, which was Southern Mississippi, and my roommate was swimming in the indoor pool. I went up to him and said, "Wes, guess what happened to me over the holidays! I got saved!" He replied, "That's great. I've been saved a long time myself." We had gone to parties and drank booze together and I certainly couldn't see Christ in his life. I decided that my life was going to be different because I was tired of straddling the fence as many so called Christians are doing. (II Cor. 5:17).

The following Sunday night I went to an independent Baptist church and Pastor C. R. Williams preached about the responsibility of Christians to lead others to Christ. I was assured in my heart and mind that I had been saved so, during the invitation, I walked the aisle and made a public profession of faith. I was baptized the next Sunday and started telling my friends I had been saved and began distributing gospel tracts. Everyone thought I had become a fanatic and they said that Harrison is just trying something new and that it wouldn't last. Well, Praise the Lord, it has been over four years now and Jesus becomes sweeter to me every day. Jesus Christ died on the cross and shed His precious blood so that we might have eternal life. I'm so thankful that the Lord allowed me to live twenty-seven years and that on that December night I dropped all pretense and opened my heart to Jesus Christ in simple faith.

How about you? On what do you base your hope of Heaven? A good life? Church membership? Perhaps you have been making the same mistake that I had made for so long. The Bible states, "Believe on the Lord Jesus Christ, and thou shalt be saved." (Acts 16:31). It is one thing to believe about a person but it is quite another thing to trust yourself to that person. I had always believed in Jesus Christ but I had never trusted him completely to take me to Heaven. There are many who believe the basic facts about the Lord Jesus Christ, (the Bible says the devils believe and tremble. [James 2:19],) but they have never committed themselves to Him. They believe He can save them but they do not let Him do it.

To believe in Christ is more than to believe historical facts about Him. It means you must turn your life over to Him and depend on Him entirely for your soul's salvation and for happiness in this life. It's a personal decision and only you can make it. Will you trust Him now and be saved for eternity? (John 5:24).

LARRY HARRISON

MY DECISION

I have confessed my sins and to the best of my ability I have trusted Jesus Christ as my Lord and Savior for eternity.